The Open Univ

Block 5

Engineering: pushing back the boundaries
Parts 1 and 2

This publication forms part of an Open University course T173 *Engineering the future*. Details of this and other Open University courses can be obtained from the Student Registration and Enquiry Service, The Open University, PO Box 197, Milton Keynes MK7 6BJ, United Kingdom: tel. +44 (0)845 300 60 90, email general-enquiries@open.ac.uk

Alternatively, you may visit the Open University website at http://www.open.ac.uk where you can learn more about the wide range of courses and packs offered at all levels by The Open University.

To purchase a selection of Open University course materials visit http://www.ouw.co.uk, or contact Open University Worldwide, Michael Young Building, Walton Hall, Milton Keynes MK7 6AA, United Kingdom for a brochure. tel. +44 (0)1908 858793; fax +44 (0)1908 858787; email ouw-customer-services@open.ac.uk

The Open University
Walton Hall, Milton Keynes
MK7 6AA

First published 2001. Second edition 2002. Third edition 2007.

Edited and designed by The Open University.

Typeset by SR Nova Pvt. Ltd, Bangalore, India

Printed in Malta by Gutenberg Press Ltd.

ISBN 978 0 7492 2356 4

3.2

Mixed Sources
Product group from well-managed forests, and other controlled sources
www.fsc.org Cert no. TT-CoC-002424
© 1996 Forest Stewardship Council
FSC

The paper used for this book is FSC-certified and totally chlorine-free. FSC (the Forest Stewardship Council) is an international network to promote responsible management of the world's forests.

Introduction to Block 5

The course so far has given you a flavour of different aspects of engineering: the importance of design, the impact of legislation, the ways in which we manufacture things. In this final block I will turn to some of the applications which are *Engineering the Future*. By this, I mean applications of engineering that will affect our lives, and be important in the way that we want to live our lives, in coming decades. I will add a disclaimer though:

> Prediction is difficult, especially about the future.
>
> (Attributed to Samuel Goldwyn)

which you may recall from Block 1.

Of course, there will doubtless be many new and important applications of engineering which have yet to be invented. However, by showing areas of current engineering endeavour, with the factors that are driving these applications forward, I hope to demonstrate to you ways in which our current engineering knowledge is being used to shape future products.

Part 1
Batteries: portable electricity from chemistry

T173 Course Team

The following course-team members were responsible for this block.

Academic Staff

Dr Michael Fitzpatrick (Course Team Chair)
Professor Nicholas Braithwaite
Jeff Johnson
James Moffatt
Adrian Demaid
Professor Chris Earl
Dr Dick Morris
Dr Suresh Nesaratnam
Dr Tony Nixon
Dr George Weidmann
Dr Kate Richenberg
Dr Caroline Pond
Professor Robin Roy

Consultants

Chris Ashley
Rodney Buckland
Dr Gavin Conibeer
Ken Reynolds

Production Staff

Sylvan Bentley (Picture Research)
Philippa Broadbent (Materials Procurement)
Daphne Cross (Materials Procurement)
Susan Datchler (Secretarial Support)
Tony Duggan (Project Control)
Andy Harding (Course Manager)
Richard Hoyle (Designer)
Lori Johnston (Editor)
Rehana Malik (Secretarial Support)
Lara Mynors (Editor)
Jennifer Seabrook (Secretarial Support)
Howard Twiner (Graphic Artist)

Contents

1 Portable power: introduction

1.1 Portable electricity

Bottled air for respiration has allowed humans to survive and operate underwater, on the top of Everest, in the upper atmosphere and in space. But what about 'bottled energy', or, more specifically, 'bottled electricity'? It is not practical for us to have to be near a fixed source of electricity every time we want to make a telephone call or tell the time. The manufacturers of electric batteries have been kept increasingly busy giving freedom of movement to our electronic equipment for communicating, leisure and computing. This part of Block 5 is about making 'bottled electricity' by harnessing the energy of chemicals.

There are probably several battery-operated devices around you right now: perhaps a wristwatch or clock, a remote control for audio or video equipment, a smoke detector or a torch. We are surrounded by electronic gadgets that rely on batteries for their energy. Often, this is because these gadgets are essentially portable devices, which will spend most of their operating life a long way from a mains socket. Batteries are also more convenient than running connections to the mains electricity supply for devices such as smoke detectors and remote controls.

Battery technology has responded well to the relatively low-power and low-energy challenges posed by cordless devices such as electric shavers and electric toothbrushes. Mobile communications and navigation have been similarly well served; see Figure 1.1. These applications consume energy at the rate of no more than a few joules per second (i.e. watts) so a 'bottle' containing several kilojoules of electrical energy ought to last for several hours.

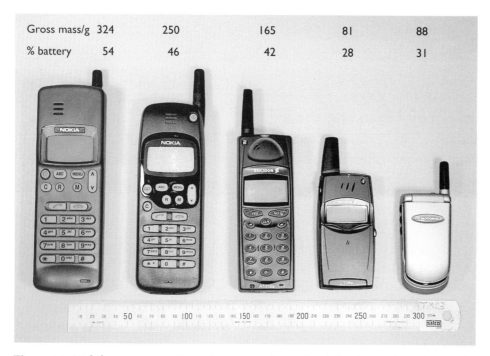

| Gross mass/g | 324 | 250 | 165 | 81 | 88 |
| % battery | 54 | 46 | 42 | 28 | 31 |

Figure 1.1 Mobile communications: four generations of mobile phone show the trends in miniaturization of electronics and of the associated battery packs (the last two phones on the right hand side of the picture are of the same generation). The ruler is graduated in millimetres, and the annotations show the mass of each phone and the percentage of the total mass that is due to the battery

At the higher-power, higher-energy end of the scale, portable electricity has been slower to make an impact. Electrically-powered transportation has been mainly restricted to 'electrified routes' such as those used for some railway lines, where power is delivered by wire. Notable exceptions are electric delivery trucks, much used in the UK's milk distribution system in the twentieth century, and various types of electric buggy that provide an alternative to walking. However, both of these examples have low speeds, and cannot travel large distances without being recharged. The big challenge for electric cars has been to match the performance and range of vehicles based on the internal combustion engine. This calls for relatively high power (typically a few tens of kilowatts) and high energy (several hundreds of megajoules), packaged in something not much bigger than a few suitcases (tens of litres).

Table 1.1 contrasts two extreme examples of demand for portable electricity. In 2001, the motor manufacturers selling electric vehicles had a choice of battery technologies that was essentially the same as that available for rechargeable batteries for electronic devices such as the CD player in Table 1.1. It is remarkable that such widely different applications should find a satisfactory solution in the same technology, but this greatly simplifies your study of this section!

Table 1.1 Power and energy in electronic gadgets and electric vehicles

	Typical power (rate of energy usage)	Typical energy stored
Portable CD player	0.5 W	20 kJ
Saloon car	50 kW	2000 MJ

In this part of Block 5 I will look at: how power is harnessed inside a battery; how the technology of batteries has advanced over many years to give us the miniature power-packs that we have today; and briefly, possible developments in the future.

1.2 Replacing a battery

Recently I had to order a new battery pack for a portable (laptop) computer. Initially, I thought that all I would have to specify was the make and model of the main unit – I was wrong. Did I want 'lithium-ion' or 'nickel-metal-hydride'? If the latter, was it the regular or the high capacity version that I wanted? To help me make an informed choice I looked up the specifications. They are reproduced in Table 1.2. (Note that in the chemical formula NiMH for nickel-metal-hydride the 'M' is a general symbol, representing *any* metal – not a specific metal from the periodic table, as in the formulae we have used previously on this course.)

Table 1.2 Battery specifications for my laptop computer

	Type I Nickel-metal-hydride (NiMH)	Type II Nickel-metal-hydride (NiMH)	Type III Lithium-ion (Li-ion)
Voltage/V	14.4	14.4	14.4
Capacity/mA h	1900	3500	2700
Operating time per charge /h	1–2	3–4	2–3
2001 Price /US$	99	129	219
Mass*/kg	0.5	0.7	0.4

* This information was not supplied by the manufacturer, although it is obviously important for portable computers. I had to obtain some batteries and 'weigh' them.

Exercise 1.1

(a) Make a reasoned choice of battery from Table 1.2 if the laptop is to be used for long periods away from a convenient mains supply.

(b) Make a reasoned choice of battery from Table 1.2 if the laptop is to be carried 'on the shoulder' daily from home to the office, over a distance of several kilometres.

You might have also been wondering why I needed a new battery pack anyway – aren't they supposed to be rechargeable? Yes, they are, but the one to be replaced was no longer functioning properly. It was not 'holding its charge'. To understand why requires some background knowledge of batteries and how they function.

I will to introduce you to the ideas behind getting electrical energy from chemical reactions (i.e. from a battery) so that we can get to the bottom of this 'broken battery' affair. As with many a good story, it is worth starting at the beginning.

Figure 1.2 shows a selection of batteries from different times. There has been a clear trend towards ever more versatile sources of electricity, packing in more energy per kilogram together with improvements in ruggedness and flexibility; meanwhile, though, environmental issues have at the same time constrained the range of chemicals involved. Over the years the pace of battery development has been set by the requirements of different users. Let's look back briefly from the present to the beginning of industrial-scale electricity to see where the idea of the battery came from.

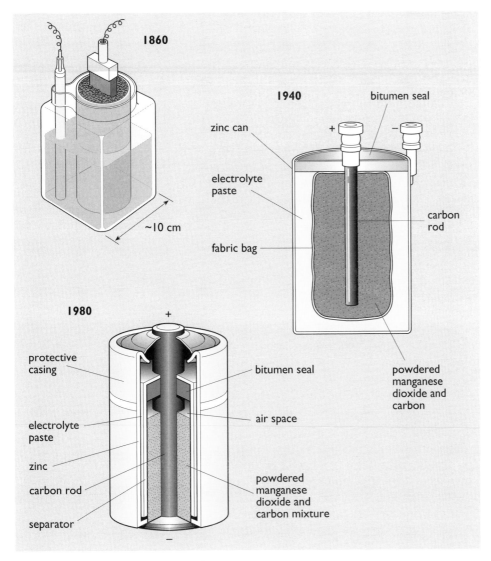

Figure 1.2 Three generations of batteries

In the 'Electro-optic Age' at the start of the twenty-first century, digital cameras, mobile communication sets, portable computers and numerous other gadgets rely on batteries as a sort of 'life support' system. Weight and size are of utmost importance in these devices – they require lightweight (portable) batteries with enough electrical energy to keep them working for at least several hours at a time. Implanted medical devices such as cardiac pacemakers make even greater demands, needing several years of capacity in a battery that cannot be much bigger than a large coin.

In the 1950s, when semiconductor technology first offered radios that were small enough to fit into a pocket, batteries were already sufficiently small that they could be classed as portable. Such portable batteries were thanks to the requirement for a portable energy source for the electric torch or pocket lamp, the invention of which was enabled by the advent of tungsten-filament bulbs – when these appeared in the early 1900s, batteries (though non-portable) were already available. An electric torch needs a steady supply of current, preferably throughout a long lifetime. Dim lights are useless, so *lifetime* was a major issue for this generation. The *shelf-life* and the *after-life* are critical too. The electricity in a battery comes from harnessing the energy generated by a process of controlled corrosion. It is important for an unused battery to remain in peak condition until it is needed, so the corrosion that will ultimately make it work must be prevented from getting underway before then. In batteries from fifty years ago, the corrosion tended to continue even when the battery remained unused, ultimately resulting in it bursting through its package – good for the torch manufacturer in the 1950s as the corrosion quickly spread, rendering the whole device unserviceable!

Earlier still, the electric telegraph was the first major consumer of electrical energy derived from batteries. The development of the electric telegraph was spurred by the expansion of railways and the requirement for universally-agreed time. By the end of the 1800s, telegraphy was calling for improvements in battery systems to give longer-range, higher-reliability signalling through cables that criss-crossed the globe. One might ask, which came first, the battery or the telegraph? The fact that the battery did by several years leaves one wondering just why anyone bothered to devise such a convenient source of electricity without it having any application.

2.1 Cats and curiosity

Necessity is often said to be the mother of invention, but this was not really so in the case of electricity. One parent of curiosity is almost certainly time, which in eighteenth and nineteenth century Europe was a luxury enjoyed predominantly by the nobility. Scientific enquiry was apparently considered a worthy pastime, and it was during this period that serious investigation into electricity began.

Electricity had a somewhat protracted infancy. Back in the sixth century BC ▼Thales▲ recorded some curious effects associated with the fossilized resin amber, which, when rubbed with silk, acquired the property of attracting tiny seeds and particles of dust. It was not until the enquiries of ▼William Gilbert▲ in the late sixteenth century that it was established that there were many other substances that could, when rubbed, produce a similar effect. One of the new combinations that Gilbert proposed for generating frictional effects (static electricity) was a glass rod rubbed with the fur of a cat.

▼Thales▲

Thales (pronounced 'thay-leez') was a Greek philosopher of the Ionic School (seventh century BC). My old biographical dictionary summarizes his thesis thus:

> The original principle of all things is water, from which everything proceeds and into which everything is resolved.

This particular view has not stood the test of time. However, Thales' observations on the curious attractive properties of ancient resin when rubbed with silk are themselves preserved in all things electrical, as the word 'electron' is a transliteration of the Greek word for amber.

I was tempted to propose that Thales was responsible for our word 'ion' to describe an atom that has a deficit or surplus of electrons – through his Ionic School. Neat but wrong! The Ionic School of philosophers were from Ionia in Asia Minor. In fact the term 'ion' comes from the Greek for 'going', describing the enhanced motion that electric fields can give to charged atoms.

▼William Gilbert▲

William Gilbert was physician to Queen Elizabeth I. At the end of the sixteenth century his curiosity led him to discover that, when rubbed, sulphur, wax, glass and many other substances behaved in the same way as amber, in that they could begin to attract small particles of dust, etc. Today we attribute these effects to 'static electricity'. It is said to be 'static' because most of the effects arise from the *presence* of electrical charges, rather than their *motion*.

Gilbert was equally fascinated by lodestone, a natural mineral that retains what we now know as magnetism.

In fact, Gilbert described how to detect 'frictional electricity' by means of 'an iron needle moving freely on a point'. It is easy to imagine how magnetism must have frustrated his early work – iron was the worst material he could have chosen, because electricity can actually cause it to become magnetic. Even so, in time he was able to distinguish electricity from magnetism and he was wise enough to leave open the possibility that these effects were nevertheless closely related. How right he was, though it was over 250 years later that the links were firmly established.

During the eighteenth century the first fruits of electrical engineering became available; see Figure 1.3. These were machines that generated electricity by winding handles that in turn rubbed disks or cylinders of glass on fixed cushions of silk or leather. Combs of metal 'swept up' the electricity and transferred it to metal rods and spheres, from which sparks could be made to fly. For those with the time and funds to be curious, these machines must have proved tremendously fascinating.

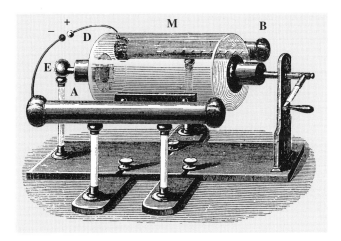

Figure 1.3 Nairne's 'Cylinder Electrical Machine' (for authenticity the annotations are reproduced as in the original drawing, from Ganot's Eléménts de Physique, but they are not relevant for our purposes)

Figure 1.4 Watson's experiments on the electrification of boys

There were so many things to find out about electricity. Why for instance, did the weather have such a profound influence on the effectiveness of the above machines? Figure 1.4 shows an example of even more ambitious research into the effects of electrifying boys!

2.1.1 Galvani (1737–98)

Under these circumstances of curiosity, it is not surprising that Luigi Galvani, a physician by training, was studying the interaction of electricity with animals. Galvani had noticed that when a dead, partially-dissected frog happened to come into the path of an electrical discharge, the leg muscles flexed, twitching the legs as though in a spasm. More curiously, sometimes the frog needed only to be *near* Galvani's electrical machine to be so affected, not necessarily directly in the path of a spark. Subsequently, it was realized that twitching accompanied nearby sparks when the spinal cord of the frog was pierced by a grounded metal (i.e. a piece of metal that was connected to the ground and so would act as a path for draining away charge). It can't have been long before Galvani was planning experiments with the ultimate spark, lightning – which, by the late 1740s, Benjamin Franklin had already shown to be electrical in nature.

This was the chain of events which led to Galvani doing experiments that involved piercing the spinal cords of dissected frogs with metal hooks and hanging them from iron railings. The railings provided the effective path to ground. It is likely that the iron of the railings would have been scraped clean to ensure good electrical contact between the hook and the railing. The plan was presumably to set the specimens in place on a stormy day and to note any correlations between lightning flashes and twitching legs. The strange result was that some legs twitched as soon as they were hung on the railing – even in clear weather.

2.1.2 Volta (1745–1827)

Alessandro Volta, a compatriot of Galvani, was also interested in the study of electricity. He read Galvani's account of a range of careful experiments, attributing the twitching of the frogs' legs to the drawing of electricity from the nerve–muscle system. Volta, in the best tradition of science, reserved his judgement pending further, independent, investigations. He fixed his attention particularly on the fact that the connection to the nerve necessarily involved two different metals being in contact. Volta must have been aware of contemporary curiosity about the peculiar things that happen when different metals are joined together. Figure 1.5 shows the sort of experiment Volta's contemporaries were carrying out – an unpleasant taste can be detected when the tongue is touched to the junction of two crossed rods of different metals. Volta went further. He placed a silver coin on his tongue and then inserted a strip of tin foil into his mouth – a sour taste sensation correlated exactly with the foil touching tongue and coin simultaneously. Some interaction was evidently taking place between the two metals in his mouth. So Volta rejected Galvani's physiological description of the cause of the twitching frogs' legs. Instead he set about seeking a purely inorganic, chemical explanation, based on the contact of different metals.

Figure 1.5 The bitter taste of electricity: touching the tongue to the 'V' formed by crossing two rods of different metals – brass and steel, for example

2.1.3 Galvani versus Volta

So, in summary, the phenomenon to be explained was this. A frog's leg appears to twitch when a brass hook through the spinal cord is hung on an iron railing, which the frog's leg also touches; the effect needs moist or damp conditions. The same effect could be replicated with the iron railing replaced by an iron rod; see Figure 1.6.

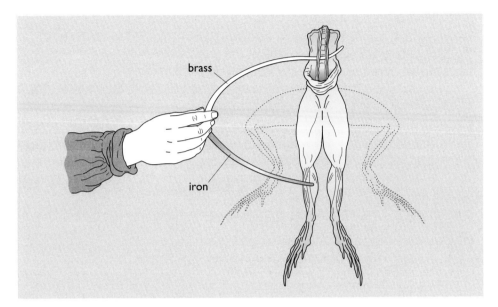

brass

iron

Figure 1.6 'Brass and iron rods drive spasms in frogs' legs', says Volta

Galvani's medically-based explanation was as follows:

> There is electricity within the body of living animals; it is important to the functioning of muscles and nerves. This electricity can be drained, even from dead and dismembered animals. One way to do so with a frog is to pierce the spinal cord with a metallic conductor. As the electricity drains away, muscle spasms occur.

Volta's position was this:

> A brass hook on an iron railing, in the presence of moisture, will generate energy capable of electrically stimulating animal tissue in contact with both metals. Applied to sensitive areas of muscle one should not be surprised to see spasms.

Galvani's group tried to refute Volta's claim by showing that the effect still occurred, although less vigorously, using *iron* hooks and *iron* railings. Volta's side discounted this, saying that the iron of the hooks was probably a different composition from that of the railing – therefore these are still 'different' metals in contact. For our purposes, it is not necessarily helpful to describe a pair of metals as being *different* if both happen to be what we want to call iron: I'll use the description *dissimilar* instead to emphasize that the pair are not identical.

2.2 Simple electrochemical cells: invention or discovery?

Before Galvani reported his work on animal electricity in 1791, Volta had been preoccupied with the static electrification of substances, deriving his electric charges from things being rubbed. The various machines (as in Figure 1.3) available could do the work necessary to separate the electrical charges involved by considerable distance, investing in them a large amount of energy. However, this energy was soon spent in brief, but spectacular, sparks.

The pulling apart of electrical charges that the machines achieved was rather like the stretching of elastic bands: strong forces build up, directed towards restoring the initial arrangement.

By contrast, Volta found that the electricity created by the contact of dissimilar metals through a chemical solution (i.e. chemical energy) appeared to be of much lower energy. It was found that although displays of sparks could be made, they were feeble. Importantly, though, these sparks persisted for as long as the metals were joined through the various chemical solutions, particularly acidic ones (see ▼Acids and alkalis▲); see Figure 1.7. Today we call an arrangement in which two metals are joined through a chemical solution an *electrochemical* cell, because what happens in the cell involves both electricity and chemistry. An electrochemical cell is the basis of all batteries.

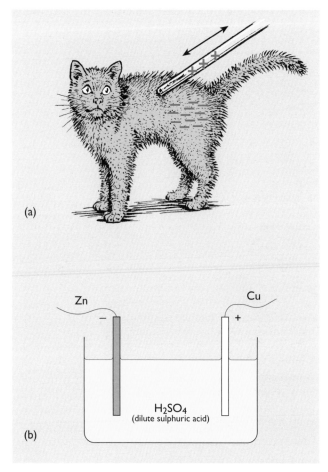

Figure 1.7 Two ways of generating an electric charge:
(a) Rubbing the fur of a cat with a glass rod (b) Joining two metals through an acidic chemical solution

---

▼Acids and alkalis▲

You will probably be familiar with the word 'acidic'. An acid is a chemical solution that has a high concentration of hydrogen ions. An alkali, which may be considered to be the 'opposite' of an acid, has a low concentration of hydrogen ions. Here 'high' and 'low' are generally taken to be relative to pure water.

Water, formula H_2O, does not have all its constituent atoms joined together as the formula suggests. In practice, some of the H_2O molecules will split apart in the water to form positively-charged H^+ (hydrogen) ions, and negatively-charged OH^- (called 'hydroxide') ions.

A solution that has a higher concentration of H^+ ions is an acid; one with a higher concentration of OH^- ions (which will tend to mop up stray H^+ ions and so reduce their concentration) is an alkali. You won't have to remember these facts, but it's useful to know the definitions.

A measure of the concentration of hydrogen ions – and so a measure of the acidity – is the pH number. You may have seen claims that shampoos are 'pH balanced with your hair'; or if you are a serious gardener, you may have had cause to check or adjust the pH of your garden soil.

Still curious, Volta discovered that not all metal combinations 'tasted' the same – their 'effectiveness' (the apparent strength of the interaction) differed. This may sound like a rather subjective approach to scientific research, but it must be remembered that the electric instruments we use today have all been developed following Volta's work. He published a list of metals in an order that reflected their efficacy in terms of strong taste:

zinc, tin, lead, iron, copper, platinum, gold, silver, graphite.

The further apart any pair were in this list, the greater was the stimulation of the taste buds. You may have experienced this effect yourself if you have traditional amalgam fillings in your teeth (based on mercury); a scrap of aluminium foil from a chocolate-wrapper or a metal fork touched directly against the filling will give the tongue a bitter-tasting twinge.

The inclusion of carbon (graphite) in Volta's list is interesting. As a conductor of electricity, graphite was apparently to be considered a metal.

Exercise 1.2

Which pair from Volta's list are likely to give the greatest sensation on the tongue?

A more convenient way to assess different combinations of materials was using electrochemical cells like the one shown in Figure 1.7(b). Volta was able to investigate this chemical electricity using techniques he had devised for frictional electricity. In light of these experiments, Volta modified his ordering of the electrochemical effects of dissimilar metals. His final order reversed the positions of tin and lead and those of silver and gold.

Exercise 1.3 (Block 3 revision)

Did Volta invent or discover the electrochemical cell?

There was a long and controversial debate among European scientists as to whether the Galvani observations were manifestations of animal electricity or were entirely accounted for by Volta's description of the behaviour of dissimilar metals. As we now know, both were right to some degree. As modern electrocardiographs – like those used to monitor heart activity in hospitals – show quite clearly, animals are electrically active. Indeed, the nerves themselves communicate by peculiar electrical means.

2.3 An inventive step – a 'battery' of cells

Having shown that electrical energy could be harnessed from dissimilar metals in contact, Volta then took his discovery on by a crucial step. He demonstrated that a pile of bimetallic discs would generate electrical energy in proportion to the number of discs in the stack. Increasing the number of discs in the stack increased the amount of energy generated.

Essential to Volta's electric pile was some moisture-bearing layer between the pairs of discs (see Figure 1.8). This arrangement was a development of a horizontal arrangement in which a number of electrochemical cells are connected in series; the 'moisture-bearing layers' were a convenient way to enable a vertical stack of cells to be built. Volta recorded his work in a letter to the Royal Society of London in 1800.

In modern terms we can recognize that the pile is a battery of cells placed in series so the electromotive force (e.m.f.) of each cell adds to the e.m.f. of the cell before it – thus making it possible to produce giant batteries. Some 3500 cells in series could drive a continuous stream of sparks through a half-

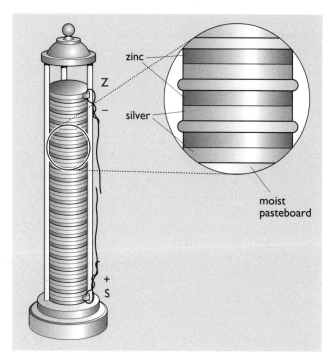

Figure 1.8 A voltaic pile: silver and zinc discs separated by layers of moist cloth pads

millimetre gap between spheres connected to each end of the pile, for several hours on end. What must have impressed the military sponsors, no doubt, was the comparison between a team of soldiers cranking an electrostatic generator and a giant box of wet discs! Unfortunately for them, the giant spark generator never turned out to be a useful battlefield weapon.

SAQ 1.1 (Learning outcome 1.1 and Block 3 revision)

Identify 'an inventive step' in Volta's work on generating sparks from the contact of dissimilar metals.

So where was the necessity that brought the invention of the battery? Well, beyond the need to satisfy curiosity, there was none. The battery had to mark time while applications were developed. One of the first major uses was in telegraph systems, such as that patented in 1837 by ▼**Cooke and Wheatstone**▲. Another early application of 'galvanic electricity', as it was called, was for the remote detonation of explosives by means of an electrically-heated fuse wire. Mining engineers and military engineers alike must have been relieved to discover that explosions could be precisely and safely synchronized from a considerable distance.

Shortly after this, a major industrial process turned to electricity to revolutionize the manufacture of domestic artefacts, by electroplating silver onto the surface of otherwise unattractive, but cheap and easily-formed metal. ▼**The Great Exhibition of London, 1851**▲ featured a vast range of these electroplated products.

▼Cooke and Wheatstone▲

Kenneth Silverman of New York University transcribed the article below from an actual copy of a provincial New York newspaper, the Poughkeepsie Journal of 13 September, 1837. See also Figure 1.9.

A NEW AND BEAUTIFUL INVENTION

An English paper contains the following description of a new and highly ingenious mode of applying the principles of electricity, or galvanism, to the communication of intelligence – or in other words, to the construction of an electric telegraph. The theory is probably correct, but we fear that serious obstacles will prevent its application to an extensive scale, as appears to be contemplated by the writer:

'When in London, a few days ago, we learned that an eminent scientific gentleman[1] is, at present engaged in maturing an invention which promises to lead to the most astonishing results, and to exert a vast influence on the future progress of society. It is an Electric Telegraph, the powers of which as much surpass those of the common instrument bearing that name, as the art of printing surpasses the picture writing of the Mexicans. The telegraph consists of five wires, enclosed in a sheath of Indian rubber, which isolates them from each other, and protects them from the external air.

A galvanic trough or pile is placed at the one end of the wires, which act upon needles at the other; and, when any of the wires is put in communication with the trough, a motion is instantly produced in the needle at the other extremity, which motion ceases the moment the connection between the wire and the trough is suspended. The five wires may thus denote as many letters, and by binary and trinary combinations the six and twenty letters of the alphabet may easily be represented. By a simple mechanical contrivance, the communication between the wires and the trough may be established and stopped, as the keys of a piano forte are touched by the hands of a practised musician, and the indications will be exhibited at the other end of the chain of wires, as quickly as they can be read off.

In the experiments already made, the chain of wires has been extended to a length of five miles (by forming numerous coils within a limited surface); and the two ends being placed near each other, it is found that the transmission of the electric action is, so far as the human sense can discern, perfectly instantaneous. Little doubt is entertained, that it may be conveyed over a hundred or a

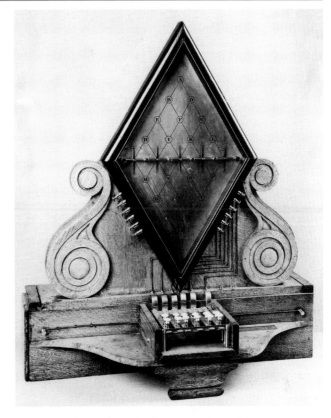

Figure 1.9 The Cooke and Wheatstone telegraph

thousand miles, with the same velocity; and the powers of the instrument promise to be as great as the action is rapid.

It will not be confined, like the common telegraph, to the transmission of a few sentences, or a short message, and this only in the day time, in clear weather, and by repeated operations, each consuming a portion of time; for, while it works by night or by day, it will convey intelligence with the speed of thought, and with such copiousness and ease, that a speech slowly spoken in London might be written down in Edinburgh, each sentence appearing on paper within a few minutes after it was uttered four hundred miles off!

There may be practical difficulties attending its operation, as yet unknown; but we speak here of what intelligent men, acquainted with the experiments now in progress, look forward to as their probable result. If the promises their experiments hold out be realised, the discovery will perhaps be the grandest in the annals of the world; and its effects will be such as no efforts of imagination can foretell.'

[1] This is assumed to be referring to Charles Wheatstone, who was backed by William Fothergill Cooke, entrepreneur.

▼The Great Exhibition of London, 1851▲

The business of Messrs Elkington, Birmingham, was built up from a patent granted in 1832 concerning the use of galvanic electricity to plate metal on to a range of products. By the time of the Great Exhibition in 1851, the Elkingtons dominated the market.

Two extracts from an article about the 'The Science Of The Exhibition' by Robert Hunt, Esq., Keeper of Mining Records, Museum of Practical Geology, makes some interesting contemporary observations on the work of the Elkingtons and the birth of electrical engineering.

In the first extract the author describes how currents from a battery can be used to transfer intricate patterns into metal – a process called electrotyping.

The principle upon which the electrotype is based has been already intimated in our remarks on Daniell's battery, but it will be well to consider it a little more closely. Under any form of battery the conditions are these: We produce or develop electricity in the battery by chemical excitement, and according to the quantity of matter which changes form within the cells, is the quantity of electricity set free, and if by wires this is conveyed to another cell, we discover that the operation of the force is such, that as much metal is deposited, as is equal, in chemical relation, to that dissolved in the battery. We have therefore only to form a surface which shall equally diffuse the electricity, to produce a uniform deposit. We may get the copper, for example, to collect in a mass around the end of a wire, or by presenting sufficient surface, diffuse over a large space, and form a very attenuated film. In copying of statues the most satisfactory mode of proceeding is to form a mould of either gutta percha [a natural latex compound], *or in the elastic* [I think he should have said 'plastic'] *compound of glue and treacle; then to well cover it on the inside with plumbago, pure black lead* [this is actually graphite, as in pencil leads]: *this forms a good surface for diffusing the deposit, and we obtain, if proper care has been taken, a perfect copy of the original. Engraved plates may be thus multiplied, the first copy from the original plate would have a raised impression, but any copy taken from this one in relief would be a facsimile of the original. The ordnance maps, suspended at the western end of the building* [the museum, presumably], *and the geological maps against the southern wall, are mostly printed from electrotype plates. Many of the ornamental blocks employed in the works of the Messrs De la Rue, have had no less than 3,000,000 impressions taken from them, and they show but slight indications of wear. These are all produced by electrotype deposit.*

Electro-gilding and plating are most important applications of this beautiful process, of which numerous illustrations are afforded. The most remarkable being those of Messrs Elkington, particularly the examples forwarded to the Exhibition by her Majesty [see Figure 1.10]. *The action is of a character precisely similar to that by which copper is deposited; but the solutions of gold and silver are more easily decomposed than those of copper, and hence less battery power* [I think he should have said 'energy'] *is required to effect the revival of the metal. The solutions usually employed are formed by dissolving the oxides of gold and silver in the cyanide of potassium; other solutions may, however, be employed.*

The applications of electricity to useful ends are numerously illustrated, and they solicit close attention from those who would learn what science is doing for manufacture.

Figure 1.10 A vase commemorating the triumph of science and the industrial arts from the Great Exhibition of 1851, featuring Newton (left), Bacon, Shakespeare and (out of view) Watt, commemorating, respectively, astronomy, philosophy, poetry and mechanics

In a second extract the author suggests that the days of merely playing with electricity (what he calls the empirical mode of proceeding) are over and the age of electrical engineering must be ushered in. Twenty years earlier in 1831 Faraday had begun to unravel the important link between electricity and magnetism.

Although satisfied that, with our present knowledge of electrical forces, we can scarcely hope to adapt the electric light to any useful purpose, within the limits of any ordinary economy, or to apply electro-magnetism as a motive power; it is quite possible that we may, by a careful study of the primary laws of these forms of electrical force, arrive at new conditions which may enable us to apply them. The empirical mode of proceeding at present adopted is of the most hopeless character. The models of electro-magnetic engines exhibited have much in them which is exceedingly ingenious; but, although working well as models, they do not promise to work with regularity or economy on the large scale; and for the present we must rest content to burn coals in our furnace rather than zinc in our batteries.

And so, telegraphers, mining engineers and electroplaters led the demand for more reliability and greater capacity from batteries; battery technology entered a development phase which still continues today.

From the 1870s electric bells caught the imagination of consumers. About thirty years later electric torches were introduced. These needed portable, non-spillable battery units. Since then, any electrical device seems to have been rendered more versatile and more mobile by ever more ingenious electrochemical schemes.

2.4 Batteries, chemistry and corrosion

Batteries such as the one Volta invented are devices put together to encourage chemical reactions between metals and ▼Electrolytes▲. These reactions are as sure to happen as a ball is to roll downhill, though it is not so easy to understand why. Suffice to say that there is such a thing as 'chemical energy' (for want of a better term!) in the same way that there is kinetic energy and gravitational potential energy. We'll get by for now with only a superficial look at the science.

The link between chemistry and electricity is not an accident. The clustering together of atoms in solids, and to a lesser extent in liquids (and barely at all in gases), is the result of the chemistry of the material in question – and this chemistry is itself affected by the electrons within the atoms. So it is both chemical and electrical.

Whenever chemical rearrangements – or 'reactions' – occur, atoms are required to swap or share electrons with each other. Energy is bound up in any arrangement of atoms. Where the result of a rearrangement binds up less

---

▼Electrolytes▲

An electrolyte is a substance that conducts electricity by mechanisms distinctly different from those in metals. Normal metallic conduction is accounted for by the drifting of electrons that are free to roam around away from their parent atoms. Conduction of electricity in this way is a defining feature of metals. Electrolytes conduct electricity through a drifting of electrically-charged atoms rather than electrons. Electrically-charged atoms are known as 'ions'. Figure 1.11 contrasts conduction in metals and electrolytes.

Many electrolytes are solutions in water or some other solvent. Strong electrolytes contain a high concentration of ions and conduct electricity well. These good electrolytes include strong acids and alkalis, and most 'salts'. A salt is a chemical compound which, when dissolved, liberates positive and negative ions from their ordered positions in the solid. These released ions are then free to carry electric charges between electrodes immersed in the solution.

A battery contains an electrolyte in either a liquid or a pasty solution. Liquid electrolytes are used in electrolysis, electroplating, and other chemical processes.

A few solids, particularly oxides, conduct electricity ionically (meaning through the movement of charged atoms) at temperatures close to their melting point. A few other substances exhibit ionic conduction when they are in a molten state. The smelting of aluminium by

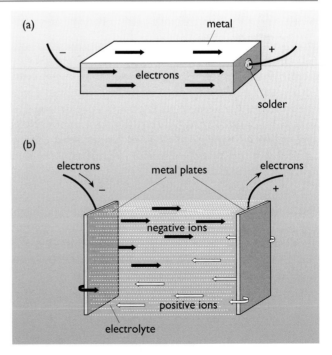

Figure 1.11 Conduction in (a) metals and (b) electrolytes

electrolysis of a molten solution containing aluminium oxide was introduced in Block 1 and described in Block 4, Part 2.

chemical energy than before, chemical potential energy is released. In some cases the energy is released as electrical energy, just as a rolling ball can transfer its potential energy into kinetic energy as it rolls down a hill. The cell within a battery is configured to intercept these transactions so that the electrical energy made available by the chemical reorganization can be gathered up. Ultimately things are arranged so that there is a separating of electrical charge, driven by chemistry. You already know (from Part 3 of Block 4) that we call the subsequent pushing and pulling of charges an electromotive force.

In the case of batteries, the chemical rearrangements involve relocating atoms *from* the electrolyte *onto* the surface of one of the 'two dissimilar metals' that Volta prescribed. At the surface of the other metal, atoms pass into the electrolyte. See Figure 1.12. The electricity is inseparable from the chemistry here as the atoms leaving the electrolyte are electrically charged (positive) and more properly called positive ions. These atoms collect negative charges from the metal as they pass from the electrolyte onto the metal surface, so becoming neutral atoms once more. Similarly atoms of the dissolving electrode leave negative charge behind and enter the electrolyte as positive ions.

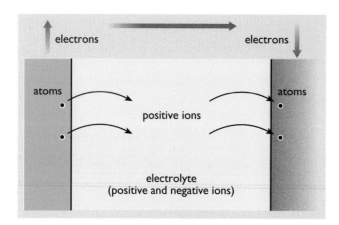

Figure 1.12 Relocation of atoms (as positive ions) from the electrolyte and electrode in a battery

A battery will be spent when all of the electrode that is giving up ions to the electrolyte has been consumed, or rather 'dissolved'. Metals that are consumed in this way are said to be undergoing corrosion. In a similar way, I am certain that the floor of my car is spent when rust has eaten right through so that I can see through it to the road. Chemically the processes in a battery and in the ▼Corrosion of steel▲ have a great deal in common: two dissimilar metals and an electrolyte are all in contact.

Chemical reactions that occur spontaneously, such as corrosion, are useful for generating energy. Sometimes, by careful design, we can divert the energy into electricity, otherwise it usually ends up as heat, light, or sound. In some cases, we can even use electricity to drive the chemistry backwards. This is the secret of rechargeable batteries, which we will come to in the next section. It's also behind a clever strategy for inhibiting corrosion called ▼Galvanic protection▲.

▼Corrosion of steel▲

Steel is not the only metal that corrodes in the atmosphere, but as a major structural metal it's the one of which we are most aware. The iron in steel was extracted from an ore in which it was in a stable chemical combination with oxygen (and to a much lesser extent with other elements). As it corrodes it is simply returning to that stable state as inexorably as a ball rolls downhill.

Corrosion occurs whenever steel is in contact with a little air and moisture, which acts as an oxygen-bearing electrolyte. The 'dissimilar metals' requirement we mentioned earlier can be provided initially by microscopic variations in the steel composition, or in the oxygen concentration of the moisture with which it is in contact.

In the corrosion process, chemical rearrangements occur because, chemically speaking, a 'more efficient' arrangement can be found which lowers chemical potential energy. That's a scientific way of saying 'look, it just happens, OK?'.

Figure 1.13 shows the process schematically, with the steel joined to a dissimilar metal to make things easier to follow. Of the two dissimilar metals, one, and always the same one for any given pair, will be the preferred local host for any oxygen and this is the one that corrodes. Atoms of this metal swap their own electrons for other negative charge (electrons) stuck to atoms of oxygen. This process, the familiar hallmark of corrosion, is marked ! in Figure 1.13. The metal atoms leave the metal and enter the electrolyte 'in search of oxygen'.

The other metal co-operates in two ways. First it takes in refugee electrons from the dissolving material; a local electric current is always associated with corrosion. See the dagger (†) in Figure 1.13. Second, it takes part in the hand over of electrons to oxygen atoms, marked *. The final products of corrosion build up in the electrolyte.

Corrosion of steel is one of the most familiar examples of oxidation, rust being a mixture of iron oxides. Oxygen has quite a reputation as an aggressive collector of two electrons per atom; in fact among chemists it's common practice to refer to 'oxidation' when atoms surrender electrons to other atoms even if oxygen isn't directly involved.

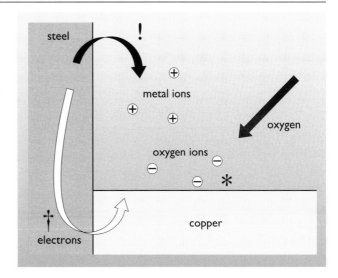

Figure 1.13 Corrosion of steel

The corrosion you are probably most familiar with occurs where one metal is an area of painted steel on a car body and the other metal is a nearby scratched area of the same material. 'Dissimilar' here extends to painted steel and bare steel. Corrosion proceeds under the paint, causing unsightly blistering (Figure 1.14).

Figure 1.14 Corrosion on a car body

▼Galvanic protection▲

When dissimilar metals are in contact in the presence of an electrolyte, corrosion may occur. Knowing this, could we use it to our advantage? We would need to know, in the first instance, which of the two metals corrodes. The answer is in Volta's ordering of bad-tasting metals that was presented in Section 2.2. Following additional experiments, still based upon taste, Volta revised the order of his list:

> zinc, lead, tin, iron, copper, platinum, silver, gold, graphite.

Taking this further, the list below is known as the galvanic series. It orders metals in terms of corrosion, and is determined by slightly more sophisticated methods than Volta's 'suck it and see'!

Chemical symbol	Element name
Mg	Magnesium
Al	Aluminium
Ti	Titanium
Zn	Zinc
Fe	Iron
Cd	Cadmium
Ni	Nickel
Sn	Tin
Pb	Lead
Cu	Copper
Ag	Silver
Au	Gold

When two of these metals are connected together, in the presence of an electrolyte, the uppermost in the list will be the one which corrodes.

Notice the similarities between Volta's list and the galvanic series. In Volta's list there are some differences in the ordering but this is probably related to the purity of the material available to him.

From the order given by the galvanic series one can pick out two familiar combinations.

(i) Galvanized steel: zinc coatings on steel afford an excellent protection against rusting; where the coating is scratched and steel (iron) and zinc are joined in the presence of water (the electrolyte) it is the zinc that corrodes.

(ii) Tin-plated steel: tin plating will prevent rusting of steel only so long as the coating remains entire; if scratched or cracked then corrosion of the exposed steel (iron) will be driven by the tin whenever an electrolyte (e.g. water) is present. Dented or scratched tin-cans are not the best packaging for food!

And here are a couple of less well known combinations.

(i) 'Sacrificial metals': zinc (or aluminium) blocks bolted to the steel hulls of large ships inhibit corrosion as the zinc (or aluminium) block preferentially corrodes.

(ii) Impressed current: because a current flows between the corroding metals a battery, or other source of e.m.f., can be used to push charges the other way, so inhibiting corrosion; see Figure 1.15.

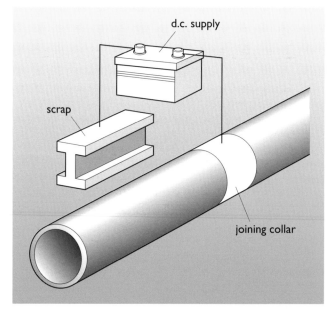

Figure 1.15 Using an impressed current to protect a pipeline from corrosion

Historically, anti-corrosion measures based on the galvanic series have been referred to as 'sacrificial anodes' and 'cathodic protection'. For our purposes, I prefer to reduce the risk of confusion with some of our electrical terminology by using the more general expression 'galvanic protection'.

3 Inside batteries

Strictly speaking, the term 'battery' means an assembly of individual cells, in each of which exists the means to produce electricity through chemical reactions. In fact, many so-called 'batteries' are only single cells; Volta's pile was a real battery (and the French for a battery is *une pile*). Anyway, I will use the term 'battery' more loosely to imply one or more electrochemical cells, in keeping with common practice.

With so many different devices requiring batteries, it is little surprise to find that the manufacturers have worked together and standardized their production. Batteries made by different manufacturers can be used in the same device. The agreed range of sizes and types is relatively small and the same class of batteries can be used to energize a range of products. However, it is not always a question of simply selecting something of the correct size, as my example of the battery for my laptop revealed – see also ▼Popular opinion▲.

3.1 Electrodes and electrolytes

There are three components in any battery: two different conductors, called electrodes; and the conducting medium between them, the electrolyte. In order to generate electricity the electrodes must be made of different materials.

Corrosion takes place at one of the electrodes. As the metal atoms (ions) slip off into the electrolyte solution, looking for oxygen ions to bond to, they leave behind negative charges (electrons) that are then available to the outside world, so this end is the *negative* terminal. This is the one that would be marked '−' on a battery. The other electrode is called the *positive* terminal and it is marked '+'. Outside the battery, the positive terminal is where electrons are gathered in from any external circuit; they are then passed inside the cell to particles in the electrolyte. (The terms 'cathode' and 'anode' are sometimes used to distinguish electrodes in electrochemical cells. I will not be using these here, preferring instead the more obvious designations 'negative electrode' and 'positive electrode'.)

Figure 1.16(a) shows a simple 'home-made' battery comprising three cells. Each cell is made by dipping a carbon rod into a tin-plated steel can containing brine; the tin coating needs to have been scratched with wire wool

---

▼Popular opinion▲

There are many different types of battery. Keeping and gaining market share forces the many manufacturers to innovate, constantly seeking an advantage over competitors. This in turn creates technological challenges for the everyday users of portable energy. Which battery for which appliance? When can we get away with the cheapest? What is the proper way to compare one claim for longer life against another for higher energy? What drains a battery quickly?

The market finds the range overwhelming. A 1998 MORI poll found as follows:

  57% can't tell a high drain application when they see one;

65% thought personal stereos were high drain devices (they aren't);

61% thought a camera flash was a low drain device (it isn't);

13% only are confident which type to buy;

78% do not want to bother deciding, and would prefer to be able to buy a single option.

The strong opinion expressed by this last statistic has not gone unheard by manufacturers. Since that poll took place the range of batteries has been reduced, with most of the common 1.5 volt non-rechargeable cells 'in the shops' by 2001 being the 'alkaline' type, which can be used in all standard applications.

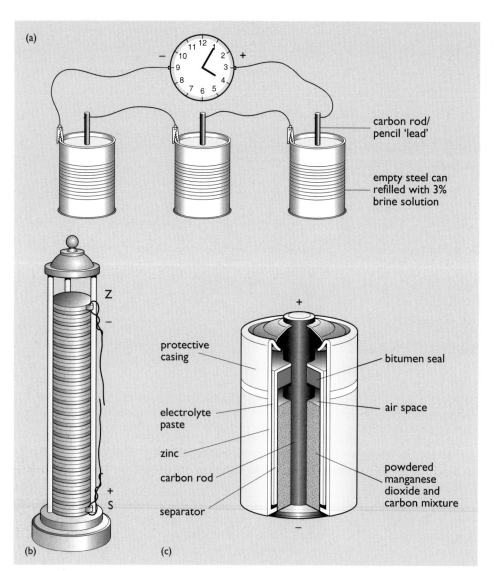

Figure 1.16 (a) The 'bean-can' clock (b) Volta's battery (c) A Leclanché battery

to expose the steel, and the carbon rod musn't be in contact with the can. The '3% brine' is a solution of 30 g of table salt dissolved in one litre of water. The cell voltage is a property of the particular materials involved. Each of the cells in this case generates an e.m.f., or voltage, of about half a volt. The connections between cells add their e.m.f.s in series, giving in effect a 1.5 V battery, which is what is typically used for a kitchen clock. Before you commit yourself to being self-sufficient in batteries I should warn you that this kind of battery needs regular can changes; furthermore, left unattended for too long, even disconnected, the corrosion of the can continues so that the rust-stained brine eventually leaks out.

SAQ 1.2 (Learning outcome 1.2)

Identify the two electrode materials and the electrolyte in Figure 1.16(a). Suggest which material is the negative electrode.

The arrangement in Figure 1.16(b) shows Volta's first battery, which was described by him thus:

> The apparatus to which I allude, and which will no doubt astonish you, is only the assemblage of a number of good conductors of different kinds arranged in a certain manner. Thirty, forty, sixty or more pieces of copper, or rather silver, applied each to a piece of tin or zinc, which is much better, and as many strata of water, lye etc. or pieces of paste board, skin etc. well soaked in the liquids; such strata interposed between every part or combination of two different metals, and always in the same order of these three kinds of conductors...

(Learning outcome 1.2)

Identify the two electrodes and the electrolyte in Volta's battery.

Figure 1.16(c) shows a cut-away drawing of a general-purpose mass-manufactured battery. The standard electrode combination in such batteries until recently was that of zinc and carbon – a pair that Volta must have noted as being a particularly potent combination, as they are at the extremes of his list. Notice how narrow the space is between the zinc can and the powdered mixture around the carbon rod. This space is filled by the electrolyte paste, made of ammonium chloride in water – an inspired choice made back in the 1860s by a French engineer, Georges Leclanché.

To understand how Leclanché's scheme works needs a little more description of the chemistry going on in his cell. In particular, we have to look more carefully into the way electric charges are transferred between the electrolyte and the electrodes.

3.1.1 Zinc and the electrolyte

At the negative electrode of a Leclanché cell, the zinc metal is in contact with ammonium chloride solution, the electrolyte. In this situation chemical energy drives the zinc to corrode. What happens is that zinc atoms on the surface of the metal pass into the electrolyte, leaving behind two electrons. Stripped of two lumps of negative charge (i.e., those left-behind electrons) the atoms of zinc have two units of positive charge and are called *ions*. Here is how we write down the negative electrode reaction, first in plain English:

Zinc atoms leave behind two electrons each to become zinc ions.

This is the same as saying:

Zinc atoms become separated into zinc ions and pairs of electrons.

In our notation of chemical symbols we write this as:

$$Zn \rightarrow Zn^{2+} + 2e^-$$

Here I am using the symbol 'e⁻' to represent electrons. So rather than showing a reaction between elements, as for the chemical equations you've seen previously, this shows an element 'splitting up' into ions and electrons. Remember that these chemical equations show the proportions in which events occur, rather than the absolute number. In truth, at any instant there are billions of ions per square centimetre of positive electrode surface leaving pairs of electrons and wandering away as ions.

So substantial numbers of zinc ions are out in the electrolyte, and more importantly, twice that number of electrons are left behind in the metal (see Figure 1.17). Charges have been separated. The metal has a surplus of negative charge and the electrolyte appears to be getting a surplus of positive charge. There is a build-up of charge associated with the abandoned electrons. So, at the same time, some of the zinc ions that have wandered off will be lured home by the attraction of the charge they left behind. On their return they pick up a pair of electrons and settle back into life at the surface as a neutral atom. Left to its own devices the process reaches a steady balance between departures and arrivals.

If an external circuit is connected so that some of the build-up of electrons can be drained away from the metal, then there is less incentive for the ions to return home. The negative electrode responds by allowing more zinc atoms to wander off in an effort to replenish the negative charge that has drained into the external circuit and restore the balance between departures and arrivals. For every two billion electrons that the external circuit draws off, one billion more zinc atoms are released into the electrolyte.

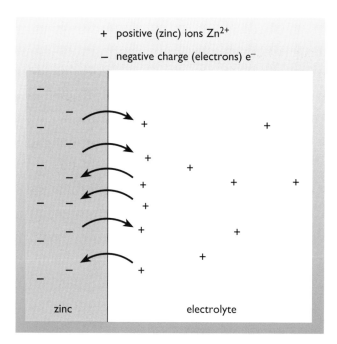

Figure 1.17 Zinc and the electrolyte

However, we now need to look also at the interaction between the electrolyte and the other electrode in order to get the full picture.

3.1.2 **Carbon and the electrolyte**

The positive electrode of a Leclanché cell is not a metal. In contact with the outside world is a rod of carbon – carbon will conduct electricity. The carbon rod is surrounded by a mixture of powdered carbon and manganese dioxide, contained by a porous membrane and filling most of the space inside the battery. This mixture is in contact with the ammonium chloride solution, the electrolyte. Exactly which of these materials is the positive electrode was only apparent once chemists had spotted what chemical reactions were occurring.

If the reaction is observed first with the manganese dioxide removed it is easier to understand what is going on. Bubbles of hydrogen gas appear on the carbon. Apparently, hydrogen ions from the water component of the electrolyte arrive at the carbon and grab electrons, becoming neutral atoms and then pairing up to form molecules of hydrogen (like oxygen and nitrogen, hydrogen goes around as pairs of atoms, H_2); see Figure 1.18. However, the gas bubbles tend to build up and form a layer of gas that breaks the electrical contact between the electrolyte and the carbon; we need a means of preventing this. The manganese dioxide's role is to do this, by acting as a 'broker' in the process of uniting the hydrogen ions from the electrolyte with electrons from the carbon. It does this by adsorbing hydrogen ions and electrons to form a new chemical compound (manganese-hydroxy-oxide). This involves large scale shuffling of the atoms and the use of powdered material gives plenty of surface area to do it in. Here is how we write it down, first in plain English:

Hydrogen ions and electrons enter into combination with manganese dioxide molecules, transforming it to manganese-hydroxy-oxide.

This is the same as saying:

Hydrogen ions and electrons combine with manganese dioxide to form manganese-hydroxy-oxide.

$H^+ + e^- + MnO_2 \rightarrow Mn(OH)O$

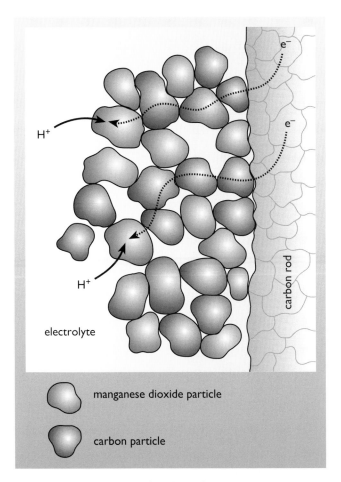

Figure 1.18 Carbon and the electrolyte

This reaction will occur as long as the carbon can be persuaded to part with electrons. As it does so, it becomes positively charged and pulling off more electrons to satisfy the appetite of the hydrogen ions becomes progressively less easy. However, should connection to an external circuit provide a supply of new electrons, the chemical reactions can be sustained.

The manganese dioxide is said to 'depolarize' the cell (that is, to stop the build-up of hydrogen that turns it off). It turns out to be rather a fickle player. Manganese dioxide recovered from different mineral deposits around the world acts with differing degrees of effectiveness. That's a factor that adds an extra dimension to competitive battery manufacture.

3.1.3 A summary of the Leclanché battery

There are good reasons for the way space is apportioned within the Leclanché cell. The positive electrode needs lots of surface area permeated by electrolyte for the manganese dioxide to do its job of preventing the build-up of gaseous hydrogen. The electrolyte must also be in contact with the negative electrode, which itself must not otherwise touch the positive electrode. An insulating mesh (separator) keeps the two electrodes apart. There is just enough electrolyte between the mesh to take up the dissolving zinc and there is just enough negative electrode (the zinc can) to match the quantity of manganese dioxide packed around the positive electrode.

SAQ 1.4 (Learning outcome 1.3)

What is consumed by a zinc–carbon battery as it generates electricity?

So to summarize, in the Leclanché battery, the negative electrode is zinc. The electrolyte is ammonium chloride. The positive electrode is a mixture of manganese dioxide and carbon and occupies most of the volume.

The negative electrode supplies electrons to the outside world as zinc atoms enter solution, becoming zinc ions. The positive electrode takes in electrons from the outside world and passes them on through the carbon to the manganese dioxide that then unites them with hydrogen ions adsorbed from the electrolyte. So the negative electrode is dissolved and we get a build-up of Mn(OH)O at the positive electrode.

Figure 1.19 shows these features for a Leclanché battery that is actively providing electric current to the outside world.

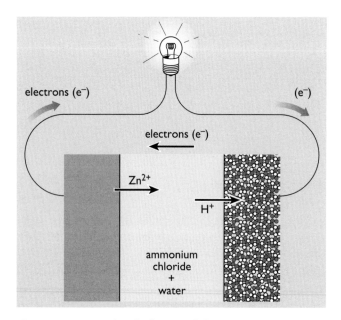

Figure 1.19 A Leclanché battery delivering current

3.2 Current and voltage

A battery produces a voltage, the electromotive force, as a result of dissimilar metals being in contact through an electrolyte. A battery produces that voltage from the instant that the parts are assembled; however, a battery will drive a current *only* when an electrical circuit is connected to it.

Current flows out of the battery as electrons supplied by the negative electrode are pushed out by the e.m.f. of the cell; the external circuit returns other electrons to the positive electrode. It is the nature of electric current in wires that billions of very slowly drifting electrons carry the current between them, so the electrons leaving the battery are unlikely ever to be the ones that return.

At the same time, a current must be flowing within the battery, transporting positive charge in the same way, from negative to positive electrode, but this time through the electrolyte. The positive ions that move into the electrolyte at the negative electrode drift away, displacing other positive ions. In fact, the positive ions that leave the electrolyte at the positive electrode are completely different ions, in the same way that the electrons entering the positive terminal of the battery are not the same ones that leave the negative terminal.

A flat battery still has dissimilar metals in contact and produces a voltage but it has lost its ability to deliver current; drawing off electrons saps the electromotive force of its strength (see ▼**Tired old batteries**▲). Just measuring the voltage of a battery may not tell you much about its condition. The real test is to see if it can deliver current, which is what a 'battery-tester' does.

▼Tired old batteries▲

Some types of battery show their age more than others in the way they perform. For instance, a cycle lamp with fresh Leclanché-type batteries starts bright, but after several tens of minutes the light shows a little yellowing as the current begins to drop, and the filament cools as a result. The next day, after a rest, the lamp may begin its duty bright once more, but the deterioration sets in sooner, and so it goes on until the best it can achieve is a useless dull yellow glow. Despite having a substantial fraction of zinc unspent, a tired Leclanché battery must be discarded.

What's happening are some complex chemical reactions involving by-products of the main negative electrode and positive electrode reactions. Two things occur.

First there is a reversible sort of ageing. This accounts for the overnight recovery. Because the positive electrode reactions that soak up hydrogen ions are slower than the negative electrode reactions in which zinc atoms enter the electrolyte, a backlog of hydrogen absorption builds up that can easily be cleared once the external circuit is switched off and the current stops. It's a bit like the race between a washer-up at the sink and the person drying items placed on the draining board: any backlog is soon cleared up once there is a break in the flow.

The other type of ageing is caused by irreversible degradation of the electrolyte owing to secondary chemical interactions between the different chemicals present. A new battery has electrolyte of a particular composition. In use, the electrolyte has zinc ions dumped into it and hydrogen ions taken from it. In my analogy with washing up this is the equivalent to the gradual transformation of fresh soapy water into a muddy soup.

Figure 1.20 shows graphically how the battery voltage would change as the battery is used in a circuit that is switched on and off periodically and as ageing builds up an internal resistance to current flow. Notice the shorter-term rest/recovery behaviour and the longer-term decline.

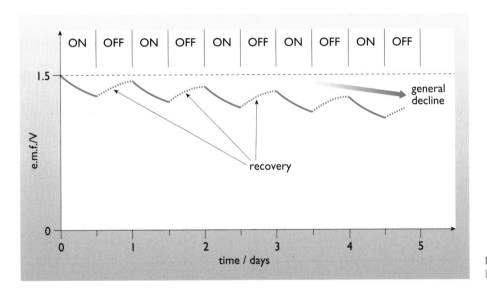

Figure 1.20 The life and times of a loaded Leclanché battery

3.3 Wet cells and dry cells

There are a number of features of Leclanché's cell that are not compatible with the requirements of my laptop. In this and the next two subsections I'm going to highlight some of these features and investigate alternative battery options.

The Leclanché cell has a major disadvantage: the liquid electrolyte needs to be contained and prevented from spilling or splashing out. An important advance was therefore the so-called dry cell version. Remember that in general, the charge movement through the electrolyte amounts to a very very slow wandering around in roughly the right direction; the ions entering the electrolyte and those leaving are not the same atoms. Therefore, there is no need for the electrolyte to be a conducting liquid; a ▼Conducting paste▲ of ammonium chloride would do. The dry cell battery is simpler to seal than a wet cell and poses much less of a problem in the event that the container is pierced.

Figure 1.21 shows a section through a modern zinc–carbon dry cell battery. The materials are labelled and you should now be able to identify the role of each. Take a moment to study it and then attempt the following exercise and SAQ.

▼Conducting paste▲

Volta had to keep his electrolyte in the layers between his pairs of discs. His way of doing this was to hold the electrolyte in a porous material. He used paper. The scheme cannot have been entirely satisfactory, as over time the paper would tend to dry out completely. The paper may also have tended to act as a wick, aiding the movement of the water and further increasing the rate at which the cell dried out. In a dry cell battery the electrolyte is immobilized by making it extremely viscous and slowing the large scale flow of material. It's easily achieved by mixing a paste of flour (or other source of starch) and water, effectively tangling the components of the electrolyte in microscopic spaghetti. The passage of current doesn't involve movement on a large scale; it is achieved by the tiny displacements of billions of ions, so a paste, rather than a liquid does the job just as well.

The term 'dry cell' is a little misleading, though clearly less clumsy than the more accurate description 'less-wet cell'.

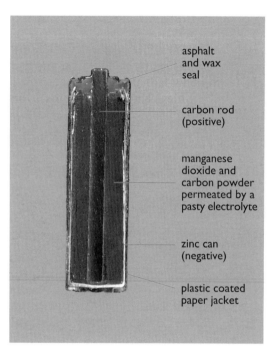

asphalt and wax seal

carbon rod (positive)

manganese dioxide and carbon powder permeated by a pasty electrolyte

zinc can (negative)

plastic coated paper jacket

Figure 1.21 A section through a modern zinc–carbon dry cell battery

Exercise 1.4

After studying Figure 1.21 complete the following tasks.

(a) To which terminal is the bulk of the enclosing case connected?

(b) Suggest three measures that have been taken to contain the chemicals in the battery.

(c) Notice how the electrolyte permeates the powder and then propose two reasons why the space assigned to the electrolyte is kept to a minimum.

(d) Physically, how would a spent battery differ from that illustrated in Figure 1.21?

(e) Is this design and construction suitable for mass manufacture?

SAQ 1.5 (Learning outcome 1.2)

In Figure 1.21 identify the following components:

(a) electrodes

(b) electrolyte

(c) the negative terminal.

3.4 Designing for life – zinc chloride and alkaline cells

The Leclanché cell has two more major disadvantages which might make it a poor energy source for my laptop. It tends to get 'tired' in continuous use, and its energy is not conveniently recoverable in full (refer back to ▼Tired old batteries▲).

Performance is affected by two types of factor. Firstly, there are those determined by the user: storage environment, operating environment and operating cycle. Secondly, there are those determined by the manufacturer: size, composition and construction.

3.4.1 Issues of use and abuse

Batteries should be kept in dry and cool conditions. Dampness could lead to an electrical path between the terminals so that the battery energy leaks away. Cool is good because chemistry tends to happen faster the warmer things get. In storage, we don't want any chemistry to happen. In use, when we do want chemistry to happen, a little warmth is no bad thing.

The operating cycle is usually determined by the job that is to be done, but where there is scope for choice, the watchwords for getting the most from a Leclanché battery are small currents and short duty. For the voltage required, one should use the battery unit with the largest volume possible, as the bigger the unit the more readily it supplies current. One might even consider alternating between a pair of batteries and allowing one to recover while the other bears the load. I recognize a demand growing from here for battery systems that are simply less fuss than this!

3.4.2 Manufacturing issues

There are several possible remedies to the problem of premature ageing of batteries that a manufacturer could investigate. The first concerns the quality and nature of materials used. Undoubtedly, a compromise is struck between the grade of material used and the performance of the product; price and its influence on market share are crucial here. As an example, it was found that simply adding zinc chloride to the ammonium chloride electrolyte improved the performance of the Leclanché cell. The first generation of 'high power' batteries in the latter half of the twentieth century was based on this.

Next, there is the question of quantity. Working within the standard range of cell sizes is an important constraint, but a manufacturer might reasonably seek to devise a way of optimizing the available volume. More compact seals at the ends of the battery, for example, would leave more space for the electrodes and electrolyte. There is also the more fundamental issue of major changes to the chemical system being used, which is what we'll cover next.

3.4.3 Alkaline batteries

The ageing problem of the traditional Leclanché battery is in the chemical reaction at the positive electrode and in the long-term degradation of the electrolyte. The options for improvement are very wide, but a couple of winners are embodied in the so-called alkaline battery. Figure 1.22 shows what this is like inside. The differences between this battery and the Leclanché battery are in the construction, and in the use of an electrolyte with a higher conductivity and more stable chemical properties – potassium hydroxide. The electrode reactions are much the same as in the Leclanché battery. The following exercise and SAQ should pick out the salient points.

Exercise 1.5

After studying Figure 1.22, complete the following tasks; the similarity with the previous exercise on the Leclanché battery is intentional.

(a) To which terminal is the bulk of the enclosing case connected?

(b) Suggest three measures that have been taken to contain the chemicals in the battery.

(c) Notice how the electrolyte permeates the powder and then propose two reasons why the space assigned to the electrolyte is kept to a minimum.

(d) Physically, how would a spent battery differ from that illustrated in Figure 1.22?

(e) Are its design and construction suitable for mass manufacture?

SAQ 1.6 (Learning outcome 1.2)

In Figure 1.22 identify the following components:

(a) electrodes

(b) electrolyte

(c) the negative terminal.

The performance of an alkaline cell lives up to its promise. It deteriorates less rapidly and enables a greater fraction of the chemical energy to be converted usefully into electrical energy. Figure 1.23 compares its performance with the earlier options.

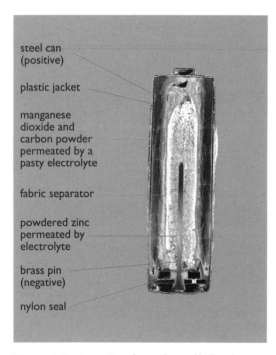

steel can (positive)

plastic jacket

manganese dioxide and carbon powder permeated by a pasty electrolyte

fabric separator

powdered zinc permeated by electrolyte

brass pin (negative)

nylon seal

Figure 1.22 A section through an alkaline battery

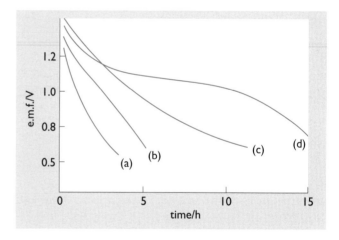

Figure 1.23 Comparison of the performance of different battery types: (a) is a standard Leclanché cell; (b) is a 'high power' Leclanché cell using refined manganese dioxide; (c) is a zinc–carbon dry cell; (d) is an alkaline cell

3.5 Primary and secondary batteries

There is a chance that the alkaline battery technology discussed in the previous section could usefully energize my laptop. However I'm not happy at the cost implications: see ▼The price of portable energy▲.

The batteries that we have considered so far are essentially 'disposable' items. When they are finished they are thrown away. In some countries ▼Disposing of batteries▲ is not so simple, and there are good reasons why used batteries should be more sensitively treated. Technically, the disposable battery is called a 'primary' battery, because it is a 'primary' source of electricity. This is not an obvious description, however, as the energy that is *obtained* from a primary battery is only a tiny fraction of that invested in the extraction and purification of the materials from which it is made. Overall, such batteries are very wasteful in terms of energy. Recycling the components of a spent battery is one way in which we could try to improve the overall energy budget. However, the chemical basis of primary batteries was not developed with this in mind and it is more efficient to start again.

A 'secondary' battery is the technical term for what the general user calls 'rechargeable', because it reuses electricity derived from the mains. The rechargeable battery is not a new idea. From the early days it was appreciated that some combinations of electrodes and electrolytes could be reinvigorated by pumping electric current back into them. This reverses the chemical reactions that take place in normal use, effectively recycling the component materials *in situ* (i.e. without taking the unit apart).

Secondary battery systems effectively store energy by converting it from electrical into chemical energy. In earlier times these batteries were also called 'accumulators' because of the way energy could be accumulated. In a secondary system, energy delivered at a low rate (low power) can be stockpiled for subsequent use at a different rate and in a different place. Once bottled like this, the energy can be carried conveniently until it is needed.

Not all battery systems involve easily-reversed chemistry. Rechargeable versions of 'alkaline' cells are available, but such are the difficulties of putting all the atoms back in the right place that at the time of writing this they were only good for about 25 charge–discharge cycles. In the following sections I'll introduce you to four common systems that are much more robust.

▼The price of portable energy▲

Mains electricity is a.c. In the UK it is based on a voltage of 230 V, varying sinusoidally with a frequency of 50 Hz. The use of a.c. is particularly convenient for transmission and distribution of electrical energy. It is also essential to certain types of electrical machinery.

Batteries, of course, are sources of d.c. energy. The use of batteries often means they have to be carried alongside or in the device they are energizing, with attendant space and weight penalties. Why use batteries at all?

Mains electricity is used for most fixed domestic appliances – refrigerators, washing machines, etc. Batteries are used to energize camcorders, personal stereos, mobile phones, laptop computers, global positioning satellite (GPS) systems, hearing aids, active medical implants and cordless gadgets. Batteries are also used for emergency lighting and electric vehicles such as motorized chairs and golf buggies, although these particular systems are distinct in being associated with high power and high energy. In all cases where batteries are used it's important that the device functions independently of a mains supply.

Table 1.3 compares portable energy with the fixed mains supply. It is clear that what you are buying when you buy a battery is portability, not energy; this is a calculation you should now be able to check for yourself.

Exercise 1.6

A particular 'C-size' battery claims to store about 30 kJ of energy. If bought in bulk they cost £1.00 each. How much more expensive is the energy than an equivalent amount drawn from the mains for which I can buy 1 kW h for £0.06? (1 kW h = 3600 kJ).

Table 1.3 Portable batteries compared with plug and socket mains

Battery	Mains
d.c.	a.c.
Fixed amount of energy	As much energy as you want
Lower power, typically a few watts	Higher energy supply rate up to kilowatts
Lower voltages: 1.5 V, etc.	230 V
Pence per joule	Pence per thousands of joules

▼Disposing of batteries▲

Some European countries take seriously the life cycles of batteries. With the rise in manufacture and use of portable electronic and electrical devices there must, after a delay ranging from months to years, be an equivalent rise in domestic end-of-life waste. We've already looked at perceived potential problems associated with lead in the solder that gets dumped when an electronic device is scrapped (see Block 3 Part 5). For many devices, a lifetime supply of batteries literally outweighs the main unit, posing disposal problems that can be many times greater.

The zinc in zinc–carbon batteries, including the original Leclanché battery, and also zinc chloride and alkaline cells, used to contain small quantities of mercury and cadmium, both of which are toxic chemicals. The addition of cadmium helps in making the zinc formable for easier processing; 'cadmium-free' is a modern boast. Adding mercury was a way of inhibiting wasteful corrosion of the zinc while the cell was not in use; the alternative is to use a purer zinc at a slightly higher material and processing cost. In 2001, 250 ppm of mercury in zinc was the statutory limit. This is rather too much for conventional zinc smelters, so specialist facilities are required to clean up the zinc before it can be fed into the conventional recycling chain. In recent years, environmental pressures have led to 'mercury-free' prescriptions.

Overall, spent zinc-based batteries are not considered a major cause for concern as the proportions of cadmium and mercury they may contain are small, and disposal in landfill sites is tolerated. Incineration of spent batteries of any type should be avoided – not only do they tend to explode but also it's better and safer not to vaporize the noxious components, but to leave them in the solid state.

Nickel–cadmium rechargeable cells pose the biggest toxicity threat in view of their very high cadmium content. They should be treated as hazardous waste. Specialist recycling plants can usefully recover the main metals economically but such plants are few in the EU; in 2001 there were none in the UK. Some argue that manufacturers of products incorporating this kind of cell should be responsible for gathering back the spent cells as part of a trade-in scheme. There is a staggeringly large amount of first- and second-generation mobile phone technology still in domestic drawers and cupboards waiting to be dumped.

Nickel could be recovered from nickel-metal-hydride batteries and the highly-reactive lithium might usefully be reclaimed from lithium-based cells; but at the time of writing no-one appeared to be making a living out of doing either.

Most of the weight of lead–acid batteries, both vehicle batteries and smaller sealed cells, is lead. They are not welcome in incinerators or in landfill sites. When I last bought a vehicle battery I was glad to be able to trade-in my old one so that the lead could be recycled, or properly disposed of.

3.5.1 Lead–acid batteries

The lead–acid battery (Figure 1.24) is the all-time champion secondary battery. It is widely used. The most obvious application is in the familiar batteries of cars. The least well known is probably in emergency standby units (e.g. emergency lighting systems). Lead–acid batteries are also used to smooth out the supply of energy of wind and solar systems.

A lead–acid battery is an electrochemical cell with a lead electrode (blue), a liquid electrolyte of dilute sulphuric acid, and a lead dioxide electrode (green). Which electrode do you suppose supplies electrons (negative charge) to the outside world?

The negative electrode gets the electrons it offers to the external world from lead atoms that busily form a deposit of lead sulphate on the electrode surface. The lead atoms become ions to form this compound and they shed electrons to do this. Here is how chemists write it, together with how to decode what is being expressed.

$$Pb + H_2SO_4 \rightarrow PbSO_4 + 2e^- \text{ (in the electrode)} + 2H^+ \text{ (in the electrolyte)}$$

Lead and sulphuric acid make lead sulphate and leave electrons in the electrode and hydrogen ions in the electrolyte.

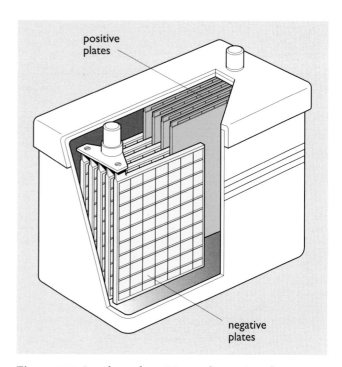

Figure 1.24 Interleaved positive and negative plates in a lead–acid battery. Porous polymer sheets between the metal electrodes give support and prevent short-circuits. The positive mesh supports a lead dioxide paste; the negative mesh supports porous, spongy, lead

At the other electrode, electrons are taken in from the outside world and made available to chemical reactions at the electrode surface. Here, too, lead sulphate is formed but this time lead dioxide is the starting material.

$$PbO_2 + 2e^- + 4H^+ + H_2SO_4 \rightarrow PbSO_4 + 2H_2O$$

Lead dioxide and electrons and hydrogen ions and sulphuric acid make lead sulphate and water.

The electrons are pushed through the external circuit while the hydrogen ions drift across the electrolyte. To recharge this type of cell you have to push electrons back in with more force than they are being pushed out; this is described by reversing the chemical equations above – the arrows in the two equations point the opposite way. Unfortunately, other things can happen too, so there's still work here for research and development teams.

Here are two engineering issues for you to ponder before we go on.

Exercise 1.7

(a) Lead sulphate is an insulator and a sufficiently thick layer will cause the battery to turn itself off. Suggest how you might try to slow the rate at which this deposit builds up on the surface of the negative electrode.

(b) Two of the by-products formed during long periods of recharging are hydrogen and oxygen, formed when water in the electrolyte is electrically decomposed. Identify any potential hazards.

SAQ 1.7 (Learning outcome 1.4)

State whether the basic lead–acid battery used in automobiles is:

(a) based on wet cells or dry cells;

(b) a primary or a secondary system.

3.5.2 Nickel–cadmium batteries

So-called NiCd (pronounced 'nigh–cad') batteries contain more than just nickel and cadmium. Figure 1.25 shows such a battery. The NiCd system enabled the introduction of a wide range of 'cordless' appliances. These are

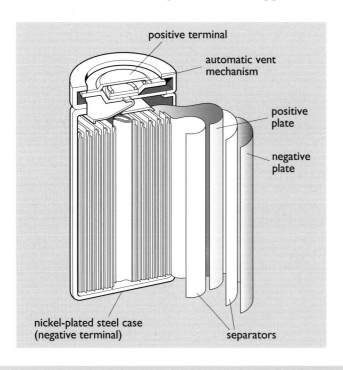

Figure 1.25 Inside a NiCd battery

gadgets, such as 'cordless' phones for use in the home (and which are linked to a land-line connection, as distinct from the mobile phones for use anywhere) that were traditionally energized by connection to the mains or another power supply. Changing the design to incorporate a rechargeable battery-pack makes the gadgets more versatile, provided that the user doesn't mind carrying the weight of the batteries.

A NiCd battery is an electrochemical cell with a negative electrode (labelled 'negative plate' in Figure 1.25) made of cadmium, an alkaline electrolyte of potassium hydroxide, and a positive electrode made of a nickel compound called nickel-hydroxy-oxide (labelled 'positive plate' in Figure 1.25).

The negative electrode gets the electrons it offers to the external world from cadmium atoms that busily form a deposit of cadmium hydroxide on the electrode surface. The cadmium atoms become ions to form this compound and they shed electrons to do this. Here is how chemists write it, together with how to decode it.

$$Cd + 2KOH \rightarrow Cd(OH)_2 + 2e^- \text{ (in the electrode)} + 2K^+ \text{ (in the electrolyte)}$$

Cadmium and potassium hydroxide make cadmium hydroxide and leave electrons in the electrode and potassium ions in the electrolyte.

At the other electrode electrons are taken in from the outside world and made available to chemical reactions at the electrode surface. Here nickel hydroxide is formed.

$$Ni(OH)O + e^- + H_2O \rightarrow Ni(OH)_2 \ OH^-$$

Nickel-hydroxy-oxide and electrons and water make nickel hydroxide and hydroxide ions.

Electrons are pushed the long way round through the external circuit while potassium and hydroxide ions drift together to reform the potassium hydroxide electrolyte. To recharge this type of cell you have to push electrons back in with more force than they are being pushed out. Then, as in the lead–acid battery, the arrows in the above two chemical equations are reversed.

Unfortunately, things can happen during repeated use that give the battery a poor retention of charge and can even lead to complete failure, so in this case too there is still further work for the research and development teams. This cyclic 'fatigue' is sometimes called the 'memory effect', as the damage accumulates cycle after cycle, especially if the cell is only subject to a shallow discharge before being recharged. A partial cure is usually effected by running the cells flat before recharging.

Exercise 1.8

What changes that take place during the discharging and recharging of a NiCd cell could possibly build up cycle after cycle leading to the memory effect? (Be as inventive as you like; there is no single right answer.)

3.5.3 Nickel-metal-hydride batteries

At first sight the NiMH (pronounced 'nickel-metal-hydride') battery is not too different from the NiCd system. There are, as ever, three chief components: an alloy electrode (labelled '–'), an alkaline electrolyte paste of potassium hydroxide, and a nickel-hydroxy-oxide electrode (labelled '+'). Electrodes and separators soaked with electrolyte are rolled up to form cylindrical cells, just as for NiCd cells (Figure 1.25).

The negative electrode in this case gets the electrons it offers to the external world from hydrogen atoms that it disgorges from the gaps between its own atoms. Hydrogen is a tiny atom in comparison with metal atoms, and in many materials it can be made to seep into the gaps between the atoms, forming what is loosely called a metal hydride. Many metals soak up hydrogen as readily as a sponge soaks up water. In effect, the hydrogen is forming an alloy with its host, just as carbon forms an alloy with iron to make steel.

In the NiMH battery, a departing hydrogen slips away, leaving an electron behind, and so launching hydrogen ions into the electrolyte. The metal used is itself usually a metallic alloy based, again, on nickel.

At the other electrode, electrons are taken in from the outside world and made available to chemical reactions at the electrode surface. Here nickel hydroxide is formed.

As with NiCd batteries, a similar, though less marked, cyclic fatigue (or memory effect) can arise if cells are repeatedly used only for shallow discharge cycles.

Exercise 1.9

NiMH cells are more robust than NiCd cells and can be discharged and recharged more rapidly. Identify one difference between the two that might account for this (be as inventive as you like, then check my suggested answer).

3.5.4 Lithium-ion batteries

The trouble with nickel is that its atoms are relatively massive, so the material density is quite high. This makes batteries heavy. The least dense metal is lithium, so a battery based on this ought to be markedly lighter.

In a Li-ion battery the principle of operation is fairly simple, but making it work has been a major challenge. The idea is that a small metal atom (lithium is the third smallest atom after hydrogen and helium) is packed into a host material that has lots of space between atoms (graphite proves useful here). This forms the negative electrode. The positive electrode is a similar, but different, material that will draw lithium atoms into its atomic-scale pores with even greater vigour than the graphite. When separated by a suitable electrolyte containing lithium ions, lithium is spontaneously transferred from the negative electrode to the positive; see Figure 1.26.

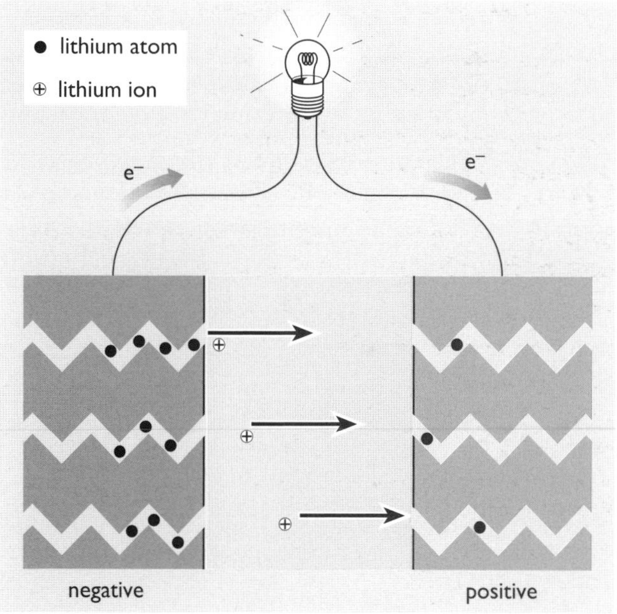

Figure 1.26 Inside a lithium-ion battery

Packing small atoms into the spaces between bigger ones is one of the things that goes on when metals are mixed together to form alloys. The electrodes in the Li-ion battery effectively form alloys with the lithium.

Recharging the cell is a bit like winding a spring. Lithium is pushed back out of the positive electrode, into the electrolyte and out of the electrolyte back into the graphite. Over-charging this kind of system can be as damaging as over-winding a spring – degradation of the host materials caused by repeated over-charging damages these cells. This is the type of battery that I originally had in my laptop computer; it may be that repeated over-charging contributed to the failure of my battery.

We won't probe more deeply into this type of cell. The idea is simple but the chemistry is complicated. As with NiCd and NiMH, cylindrical cells are made by rolling up a four-deck sandwich separator: positive electrode, separator, negative electrode, with pasty electrolyte permeating the separator.

SAQ 1.8 (Learning outcome 1.5)

By completing the following table, compare the Li-ion and lead–acid batteries in terms of the chemical changes that store and release energy.

	Lead–acid	*Li-ion*
Store	Lead sulphate is decomposed on each electrode to form lead dioxide (+) and lead (−).	
Release		Lithium leaves the negative electrode and enters the positive electrode.

3.5.5 'Smart' charging

Recharging a battery involves reversing a particular set of chemical reactions. Unfortunately, this is difficult to control precisely, and in pushing energy into the desired chemical changes, other, less desirable, things can happen. Initial charging of a secondary battery reverses the discharge process more or less exactly as it is required to. However, as the battery approaches its fully-charged state, those less desirable chemical changes become more difficult to avoid, so it is not a bad idea to proceed with caution as a full charge is approached.

Some secondary batteries, such as lead–acid cells, charge well from a supply of constant potential. Others, such as NiCds, are better charged from a constant current. No system can simply be charged 'in a flash' – the chemistry doesn't work like that – and none reacts well to persistent overcharge.

What is needed is a supervised recharging process in which the charge is stored as quickly as possible without overcharge. To do this, the charger monitors current, voltage and temperature and adjusts the rate of recharge according to a set of rules specific to each battery technology.

4 Choosing a battery

Table 1.4 reproduces data for common domestic AA-size batteries featuring the different technologies readily available in 2001. There are even more options than in my original quest for a new battery for my laptop. In fact, even if the other specifications were correct, none of those batteries in Table 1.4 would be adequate for my computer, because my laptop uses a ▼**Built-in battery**▲ that is integrated into the structure of the case rather than being based on one of the standard packages.

Table 1.4 Specifications for AA batteries

	Type I Zinc chloride	Type II Alkaline	Type III Lithium[*]	Type IV Rechargeable alkaline	Type V NiCd[****]	Type VI NiMH
Voltage/V	1.5	1.5	1.5	1.5	1.2	1.2
Relative capacity[**]	1	2.2	6.5	1.3	0.45 (0.9)	1.2
Capacity/mA h	1100	2400	7200	1400	500 (950)	1300
Recharge cycles	DO NOT RECHARGE	DO NOT RECHARGE	DO NOT RECHARGE	25 times	3000 times	500–1000 times
Time to recharge/h				12	5	8
Relative price (2001)	1	1.5	10	3	3 (4.5)	6.5
Relative weight[***]	1	1.1	0.76	1.1	0.9	1.3

[*] This is a primary battery, not to be confused with the lithium-ion secondary system.
[**] Capacity relative to a zinc chloride battery.
[***] A single zinc chloride cell has a mass of 21 grams.
[****] The figures in brackets are for a 'high-performance' NiCd battery.

▼Built-in battery▲

Building power-packs from standard size batteries is a major constraint on designers of electronic devices, especially if the batteries occupy a significant amount of space. There are various ways to push back the boundaries to make the batteries more compact.

We could reduce the size of batteries by developing new, more powerful electrochemical schemes, or we could seek more efficient ways to use energy within the devices. Another way is to abandon the standard sizes and build special batteries into each device. It would be so much more convenient if the battery in a portable device could be wrapped around other functional bits, or built into whatever spaces were left after the other parts were in place. This is what the mobile phone industry has been doing; so too have the makers of laptop and palm-top computers. Early batteries were jar-shaped because they were constructed from convenient laboratory apparatus and this cylindrical shape has remained a feature of the 1.5 V Leclanché cells. Flatter shapes were more easily achieved once the dry cell concept took off. In fact, modern batteries are really two-dimensional: negative electrode sheet, electrolyte paste and separator sheet, positive electrode sheet. See Figure 1.27.

A useful development for the built-in approach is a battery technology based on polymeric materials. Don't be surprised if one day soon the battery and the case of a device become one and the same thing.

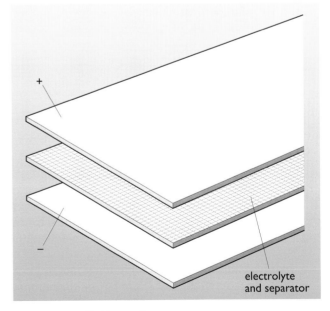

Figure 1.27 A 'flat' battery?

4.1 The correct voltage

Selecting the correct batteries for a device ought to be fairly straightforward. You simply replace like with like. With the more common batteries this is made particularly simple by the standardization of sizes and types. There is, however, a slight mismatch between primary and secondary cells which is evident in the voltage data for the rechargeable batteries in Table 1.4. As a result, the substitution of secondary batteries for primary ones leads to devices being supplied from a 20% lower voltage. Such a reduction in operating voltage occurs anyway as a primary battery ages, so the designers have already ensured that the effects are tolerable.

Example

(a) Using data from Table 1.4, determine the number of NiCd cells that are required to supply a circuit designed for 6 V and compare with the figure for any of the primary cells.

(b) Explain why a torch designed to run off two AA alkaline cells, in series, might appear a little less bright and last for less time when run from a pair of AA NiCd cells.

Answer

(a) Since 6/1.2 = 5, five cells in series will give 6 V. Devices tend to be designed to take four batteries, so in practice you have to live with poorer performance.

(b) Two NiCd cells in series give 2.4 V, whereas the design calls for 2×1.5 V = 3 V; using NiCd cells, there is less e.m.f. to push current through the bulb, so both current and voltage will be less, leading to a slightly dimmer light. However, the NiCd cells hold their ability to supply current better than an ageing primary cell, so before long, the secondary cell may be more agreeable. The secondary battery must be recharged long before the primary is spent, though, because it has a smaller capacity (Table 1.4).

SAQ 1.9 (Learning outcome 1.6)

(a) Using data from Table 1.4, determine the number of NiMH cells that are required to supply a circuit designed for 6 V.

(b) Explain why a radio designed to run off two AA alkaline cells might never sound quite as loud when run from a pair of AA NiMH cells.

4.2 Capacity

The capacity of a battery is usually measured in terms of the product of current and time, for example 'so many milliamp hours' (mA h). This gives a crude idea of ability of the battery to supply current over a period of time. Normally we'd expect to be using batteries for several hours. A capacity of 1100 mA h can be interpreted as being adequate for a job requiring 110 mA for 10 h, or 55 mA for 20 h. It would be wrong to extrapolate in the other direction and expect to be able to extract around one amp for one hour, or worse still, ten amps for six minutes; the chemistry at the electrodes and in the electrolyte can't move the atoms around fast enough for that. If you actually want that much current, there are two options. You could use many batteries in parallel: ten 1100 mA h batteries side by side are equivalent to an effective capacity of 11 000 mA h, and with each delivering 100 mA a current of 1 A is more easily achievable. Alternatively, you could just buy a bigger unit, one that has sufficient capacity within a single package.

The capacity of a battery actually gives a measure of the energy stored, but not in our normal energy units of joules. To get to the stored energy in joules two simple steps are required. First the capacity in milliamp hours must be converted into amp hours by replacing the 'milli' with 10^{-3} and thence into watt hours (W h) by multiplying the battery voltage by the battery capacity. The zinc chloride battery in Table 1.4 stores:

$$1.5\ V \times (1100 \times 10^{-3}\ A\ h) = 1.55\ W\ h$$

Then to recover the value of that energy in joules we must replace the hour by 3600 seconds. Then the zinc chloride battery in Table 1.4 stores

$$1.55 \times 3600 = 5580\ W\ s = 5580\ J$$

$$= 5.58\ kJ$$

In comparing different technologies for portable energy, a useful figure is the so-called *gravimetric capacity*, the amount of energy per unit mass. Common practice is to make the comparison in units of W h kg^{-1}.

Example

(a) Using data from Table 1.4, calculate the energy stored in a fully charged NiCd cell and compare it with that stored in a primary alkaline cell.

(b) Estimate how many AA NiCd cells should be used to provide adequate power for two hours to a device that consumes on average 5 W.

(c) Compare the gravimetric capacities of NiCd and alkaline batteries using the data in Table 1.4. (Remember that the masses in the table are given relative to the mass of 21 g for the zinc chloride cell.)

Answer

(a) The lower performance NiCd battery will store 500 mA h, which will be pushed out at 1.2 V. The stored energy is the product of these two:
energy = $1.2\ V \times 500 \times 10^{-3}\ A\ h = 600 \times 10^{-3}\ W\ h$
Putting 1 h = 3600 s will give the energy in joules:
energy = $(1.2 \times 500 \times 10^{-3}) \times 3600\ W\ s = 2160\ J\ = 2.16\ kJ$
By contrast the alkaline battery stores: $(1.5 \times 2400 \times 10^{-3}) \times 3600\ J = 12\ 960\ J$
= 13 kJ.
I'd expect to be recharging NiCd batteries at least six times as often as I would otherwise replace alkaline batteries.

(b) Five watts for two hours consumes $5 \times 2 \times 3600\ J = 36\ 000\ J$. Since each NiCd battery will store 2.16 kJ we'll need at least 36/2.16 = 16.67 cells – so let's round up to 17. This shows that you'd be better using the bigger C- or D-size cells, which have a greater capacity!

(c) The mass of the NiCd cell is $0.9 \times 0.021\ kg = 0.019\ kg$. Its gravimetric capacity is $1.2 \times 500 \times 10^{-3}\ W\ h\ /\ 0.019\ kg = 31.6\ W\ h\ kg^{-1}$.

SAQ 1.10 (Learning outcomes 1.5 and 1.9)

(a) Using data from Table 1.4, calculate the energy stored in a fully charged NiMH battery and compare it with that stored in a primary lithium cell.

(b) Estimate how many NiMH AA cells should be used to provide adequate power for 40 hours to a device that consumes on average 0.5 W (e.g. my portable CD player).

(c) Compare the gravimetric capacities of NiMH and lithium primary batteries using the data in Table 1.4. (Remember that the masses in the table are given relative to the mass of 21 g for the zinc chloride cell.)

5 Carrying electrical energy into the future – replacing the battery

In this first part of Block 5 we have been looking at getting energy from electricity, with a particular emphasis on portability for information and communications technology. The idea of 'portable energy' might conjure up images of lonely explorers up mountains or in outer space, but often the range is considerably shorter. A remote control for a TV or a cordless power tool will probably never stray far from mains supplies; for these devices portability is desirable because of the inconvenience of running supply lines over the last few metres.

Portability is an important issue for electronic gadgets and, at the other end of the spectrum, for electric vehicles; the technological challenges of efficient electric traction from batteries are similar to those we have examined here. As with batteries for electronic devices, a high ratio of capacity to weight is important because an electric vehicle has to carry the weight of its own batteries.

There are two major differences, however. First, traction batteries must store serious amounts of energy and deliver it at a high rate (I estimate that when full my car fuel tank holds a chemical potential energy equivalent to 1800 MJ, and the engine can deliver a steady 50 kW of power, so that gives me about ten hours of motoring – in comparison, two AA-size NiCd batteries store about 5 kJ). Second, the use of primary cells is ruled out – can you see why (check the estimate of the price of battery energy in Section 3)?

By contrast, there are places where the use of secondary cells can be ruled out. Active medical implants for instance, such as cardiac pacemakers, are most comfortably installed with on-board primary batteries. Here long-life and zero-maintenance are essential characteristics. A clear means of remotely assessing the health of the battery is also desirable. This topic is explored further in Part 3 of this block.

One of the main development areas for portable energy technology throughout the second half of the twentieth century was the exploration of space. This will continue to be a fertile area as increasingly complicated electronic systems are sent out further from Earth, and are required to have longer operating lives.

There are two relatively new options that offer alternatives to conventional primary and secondary batteries for portable energy. Both were pioneered for space missions and are now being engineered for terrestrial use in traction and in energizing electronic devices. One offers recharging as fast as you can recharge a petrol or diesel engine by filling the tank; these are so-called ▼Fuel cells▲. The other offers a fair-weather companion that provides in daylight all the energy you need, and more for a rainy day and at night; solar cells are the main topic of the next part of this block.

SAQ 1.11 (Learning outcome 1.7)

Suggest three different devices that have demanded technological advances in battery systems.

▼Fuel cells▲

In batteries, whether primary or secondary, the electrodes are to some extent consumed as part of the electrochemical reactions that take place. A fuel cell is an electrochemical system that does not consume its electrodes, but uses a separate supply of chemical energy instead. The advantage is clear. Refuelling takes the place of recharging or replacement.

Are there really systems that will convert the chemical energy of a fuel into electricity, directly, without flames? The answer is 'yes – and not only will they do that conversion without any flames, but they do it silently too'.

Here is the burning option for a fuel such as the simple alcohol known as methanol ('alcohol' is a general term for a series of chemicals, like the hydrocarbons we saw earlier, but based on carbon, hydrogen and oxygen; the 'alcohol' in alcoholic drinks is properly called 'ethanol').

$$2CH_3OH + 3O_2 \rightarrow 2CO_2 + 4H_2O$$

Methanol burns in oxygen to form carbon dioxide and water.

The fact that methanol burns is a sure sign that the chemical rearrangement into carbon dioxide and water liberates energy. To get the reaction going, a little thermal energy from a spark is required. Thereafter the reaction proceeds, releasing heat in a flame.

Of course, we can harness the energy from burning fuels, as is done in conventional power stations. However, the process is inefficient, and a means of harnessing all the chemical energy, without losses, would be hugely advantageous.

The challenge for electrochemical engineers is to divert the reaction from thermal combustion, via an electrochemical route, to arrive at the same products. It has long been recognized by chemical engineers that platinum is remarkably effective at promoting chemical changes: it is called a catalyst (these were mentioned back in Block 1). Platinum has the astonishingly useful property of facilitating chemical reactions, without itself being used up in the process. It is no surprise to find platinum at the start of the non-thermal route in question. The use of a catalyst allows the reaction to bypass the normal burning that occurs if thermal energy is used to trigger the reaction between methanol and oxygen.

$$2CH_3OH + O_2 \xrightarrow{Pt} 2CO_2 + 8H$$

Methanol and oxygen at the surface of a platinum (Pt) catalyst form carbon dioxide and hydrogen.

This reaction frees up hydrogen atoms. In a fuel cell, it must take place at or even within the negative electrode. The second part of the reaction is the electrical bit. Hydrogen atoms are transferred from the negative electrode, as hydrogen ions, into an electrolyte; in so doing the atoms leave an electron behind in the negative electrode. The hydrogen ions move through the electrolyte to the positive electrode where they combine with oxygen from the air and electrons from the external circuit to form water.

At the negative electrode:

$$8H \rightarrow 8H^+ + 8e^- \text{ (into the external circuit)}$$

At the positive electrode:

$$8H^+ + 2O_2 + 8e^- \text{ (from the external circuit)} \rightarrow 4H_2O$$

What this process needs is an electrolyte that will conduct hydrogen ions (but not electrons, which must pass around the external circuit), and platinum-coated electrodes that are permeable to oxygen. One material for the electrolyte is a polymer membrane, engineered to have the right porosity.

Just as with primary and secondary batteries, there are many different approaches. Different fuels can be used, ranging from pure hydrogen to unleaded petrol, each different fuel requiring a particular approach. High-power, fixed installations inevitably differ in detail from portable cells, but the overall principles are the same.

Fuel cells were devised for use in space vehicles. In the old fashioned, high-cost technology of space they were a satisfactory but expensive means of producing electricity. In the future, the terrestrial market for portable energy in telecommunications and transportation will be more than enough to bring fuel cells technology back to Earth as a mainstream alternative to secondary batteries.

6 Learning outcomes

After studying this part of Block 5 you should be able to do the following.

1.1 Recognize key steps in the invention of batteries.

1.2 Identify the basic components of a primary battery.

1.3 Discuss the electrochemical links between batteries and corrosion.

1.4 Distinguish between wet and dry batteries and between primary and secondary batteries.

1.5 Choose a battery for a particular task, given relevant data.

1.6 Outline the general principles of rechargeable batteries.

1.7 Identify various factors that have driven the development of common batteries.

1.8 Improvise a simple battery based on carbon rods, brine and steel cans.

1.9 Perform simple calculations related to battery selection.

Answers to exercises

Exercise 1.1

(a) I'd choose Type II, the one with the largest capacity and hence longest operating time, although the actual period of operation may be short enough to get away with one of the others (cheaper or lighter).

(b) I'd choose Type III, the lightest one, if I could afford it; a fitter, meaner colleague opted for Type I, the cheapest, on the grounds that the laptop is apparently always used where it can be plugged into the mains, at home and in the office, so battery performance barely matters!

Exercise 1.2

Zinc and graphite, being furthest apart, are likely to produce the greatest effect.

Exercise 1.3

It looks like discovery to me. There was no real application for such a cell at that stage.

Exercise 1.4

(a) The zinc can that forms the negative (bottom) terminal envelops the construction.

(b) You may have spotted three of these: the electrolyte is made pasty; the zinc can encloses the bulk of the assembly; a wax ring and asphalt form a seal around the lid; a plastic jacket is wrapped around the whole.

(c) The electrolyte separates the negative and positive electrode materials and provides an ionic conduction path (zinc ions enter at the negative electrode and hydrogen ions leave at the positive electrode): (i) any extra distance between the two just adds undesirable electrical resistance; (ii) any extra volume occupied by electrolyte adds undesirable weight and decreases the 'payload' of consumable electrode material.

(d) In a spent battery the zinc can is corroded away so it would be thinner and punctured. Also, the manganese dioxide is partly transformed to manganese-hydroxy-dioxide (but you might not know to look at it). In fact, the electrolyte might also look less homogeneous (smooth and uniform) as by-products of the negative and positive electrode reactions build up within it.

(e) Clearly the design and construction details have evolved precisely so that it is compatible with mass production but there will be some conflicts of interest. (For example the zinc you'd choose on electrical grounds would be high purity material, whereas the zinc that is most easily formed to shape has controlled additions of other elements.)

Exercise 1.5

(a) The steel can that forms the positive (top) terminal envelops the construction.

(b) You may have spotted three of these: the electrolyte is made pasty; a steel can encloses the bulk of the assembly; a metal washer and nylon form a seal around the base; a plastic jacket lines the outside of the can, also providing electrical insulation.

(c) The electrolyte separates the negative and positive electrode materials and provides an ionic conduction path (zinc ions enter at the negative electrode and hydrogen ions leave at the positive electrode): (i) any extra distance between the two just adds undesirable electrical resistance; (ii) any extra volume occupied by electrolyte adds undesirable weight and decreases the 'payload' of consumable electrode material.

(d) In a spent battery, the central zinc negative electrode is corroded away so it would be thinner and punctured. Also, the manganese dioxide is partly transformed to manganese-hydroxy-dioxide (but you might not know to look at it). In fact the electrolyte might also look less homogeneous (smooth and uniform) as by-products of the reactions at the electrodes build up within it.

(e) Yes. Clearly the design and construction details have evolved precisely so that an alkaline battery is compatible with mass production, but there will be some conflicts of interest.

Exercise 1.6

The battery offers energy at 30 kJ per £1.

The mains offers 3600/0.06 kJ = 60 000 kJ per £1, which is 60 000/30 = 2000 times cheaper than joules from a battery.

Exercise 1.7

(a) The electrodes need to have a high surface area to keep the growing deposit as thin as possible. In practice, the electrode plates are made from porous structures with lots of surface area.

(b) First, if water is being decomposed into gases then the concentration of remaining electrolyte is increasing and the level of liquid is decreasing. Second, hydrogen can react explosively with oxygen, so you must either prevent gas formation (divert the chemistry via some other route) or else contain the gases once they are formed.

Exercise 1.8

Here's my guess. Suppose in the discharge it is mostly the 'old' nickel-hydroxy-oxide material that is 'transformed' into 'fresh' nickel hydroxide as the cell discharges and during the recharge phase it is mostly 'old hydroxide' that is transformed into 'fresh' nickel-hydroxy-oxide. Then frequent charge–discharge cycles would be effectively moving material around and changing the shape of the bits inside, making rough bits smooth or smooth bits rough. That'll probably mess it up a bit. Anyway, I can see how a good heavy discharge might cure it.

Exercise 1.9

Here's my guess. Hydrogen is readily moved in and out of the spaces between the atoms of the electrode metal in NiMH cells. This is the simplest of atomic rearrangements and considerably simpler than the reaction at the negative electrode of a NiCd cell, so presumably there is less movement of material during the charge and discharge cycles that could degrade the cell.

Answers to self-assessment questions

SAQ 1.1

There are in fact two inventive steps that can be identified. The first is the construction of the pile to form an additive combination of individual electrochemical cells. The second was the use of moist pads to join successive elements.

SAQ 1.2

Electrodes: tin-plated steel and carbon; steel is the negative electrode apparently, because it is the one that corrodes, making negative charges available to the outside world; it is marked '−'. The carbon rod will be the positive electrode.

Electrolyte: brine.

SAQ 1.3

Electrodes: 'copper, or rather silver' and 'tin or, better, zinc'.

Electrolyte: the lye, being a liquid of dissolved washing soda.

SAQ 1.4

The zinc electrode corrodes as a consequence of zinc atoms dissolving in the electrolyte. At the other end of the system, manganese dioxide is consumed (as it transforms to manganese-hydroxy-oxide) as electrons transferred to it enable the adsorption of hydrogen ions.

SAQ 1.5

(a) Carbon rod in manganese dioxide/carbon powder.

Zinc can.

(b) The ammonium chloride paste.

(c) The can accepts electrons as the zinc atoms dissolve, so it is the negative terminal.

SAQ 1.6

(a) Manganese dioxide/carbon powder and the steel can that surrounds it.

Zinc powder running up the central axis and the brass pin that it encloses.

(b) The potassium hydroxide paste.

(c) The brass pin accepts electrons as the zinc atoms dissolve, so it is the negative terminal.

SAQ 1.7

(a) The electrolyte, dilute sulphuric acid, is a liquid: wet cell.

(b) The system is rechargeable: secondary.

SAQ 1.8

	Lead–acid	Li-ion
Store	Lead sulphate is decomposed on each electrode to form lead dioxide (+) and lead (–).	Lithium leaves the positive electrode and enters the negative electrode.
Release	At the negative electrode lead reacts to form lead sulphate. At the positive electrode lead dioxide reacts to form lead sulphate.	Lithium leaves the negative electrode and enters the positive electrode.

SAQ 1.9

(a) Since 6/1.2 = 5, five cells in series will give 6 V.

(b) Two NiMH cells in series give 2.4 V, whereas the design calls for 2×1.5 V = 3 V; using NiMH cells there is less e.m.f. to push current through the output of the radio, so both current and voltage will be less, leading to a slightly lower maximum volume. However, the NiMH cells hold their ability to supply current better than an ageing primary cell so before long, the secondary cell may give more agreeable sound levels. The secondary battery must be recharged long before the primary is spent.

SAQ 1.10

(a) The NiMH battery will store 1300 mA h, which will be pushed out in use at 1.2 V. The stored energy is the product of these two:

energy = 1.2 V $\times 1300 \times 10^{-3}$ A h = 1.56 W h

Putting 1 h = 3600 s will give the energy in joules:

energy = $(1.2 \times 1300 \times 10^{-3}) \times 3600$ W s = 5616 J = 5.6 kJ

By contrast, the primary lithium battery stores:
$(1.5 \times 7200 \times 10^{-3}) \times 3600$ W s = 38 880 J = 39 kJ.

I'd expect to be recharging NiMH batteries at least seven times as often as I would otherwise have to replace lithium batteries.

(b) Half a watt for forty hours consumes $0.5 \times 40 \times 3600$ W s = 72 000 J. Since each NiMH will store 5.6 kJ we'll need at least 72/5.6 = 12.86 cells – so let's round up to 13. This shows that you'd be better off using C or D cells! Interestingly, based on the 'four alkaline batteries' specified by the manufacturer of my CD player, I don't seem able to get more than 30 of the 40 hours of playback advertised, i.e. 54 of the required 72 kJ; I'm tempted to ask them to prove their claim.

(c) The mass of the NiMH cell is 1.3×0.021 kg = 0.027 kg. Its gravimetric capacity is $1.2 \times 1300 \times 10^{-3}$ W h / 0.027 kg = 57.8 W h kg^{-1}.

The mass of the Li cell is 0.76×0.021 kg = 0.016 kg. Its gravimetric capacity is $1.5 \times 7200 \times 10^{-3}$ W h / 0.016 kg = 675 W h kg^{-1}.

SAQ 1.11

You may have chosen three from this list of topics that I have covered in this part of Block 5.

Electric telegraph

Electroplating   Mobile communications   Medical implants

Door bells   Laptop computer   Space exploration

Pocket lamp/torch   Electric vehicles

Part 2
Electricity from sunlight

Contents

1 Introduction

We have just looked at batteries as chemical sources and stores of energy. We will now look at another way in which energy can be generated without chemistry.

We have had means of producing energy from fossil fuels for many decades, and from nuclear reactions since the 1960s; but what about one of the current engineering challenges – power from sunlight?

Solar radiation can be harvested directly in two ways: either as heat, or as electricity. Here we will concentrate on the direct generation of electricity. ▼Photovoltaics▲ (or PV), the current technology for achieving this, has many advantages compared to other sources of electricity. It is modular, virtually maintenance free and suitable for urban and remote applications alike – you might have said the same about batteries, so watch out for the differences.

Photovoltaic cells are convenient for some portable power systems: pocket calculators have used low performance cells for many years; the exploration and exploitation of space would be considerably more expensive and difficult

---

▼Photovoltaics▲

Like the words 'news' and 'electronics', I will be using 'photovoltaics' as a singular plural. It sounds awkward at first. Electronics *has* played a major part in the technological revolution of recent years. Photovoltaics *is* a major subset of electronics. The true worth of photovoltaics is yet to be fully realized.

The term 'photovoltaic' derives from the Greek word for light – photo – and the term volt for electromotive force. So photovoltaic implies an electromotive force from light.

The photovoltaic effect was first observed by the French scientist Alexandre Edmond Becquerel in 1840, who noticed an increase in a wet battery's voltage when its silver plate electrodes were exposed to light. In 1877 the photovoltaic effect was observed in the solid material selenium. In 1883 an American, Charles Fritts, made a selenium photovoltaic cell, but it was very inefficient, converting less than 1% of light falling on it into electricity.

It was to take the revolution in understanding of the fundamental properties of materials and of light in the early twentieth century to explain these effects. The development of modern cells had to await the electronics revolution of the 1950s. Chapin, Fuller and Pearson of Bell Labs produced the first silicon cell in 1953. By the following year a cell efficiency (the ratio of electrical output to incident solar power) of 6% was achieved.

Photovoltaic solar cells (see Figure 2.1) have been used for power in space since the launch of the *Vanguard 1* satellite in 1958. These cells are the power source of choice for space missions within the solar system because of their high reliability and zero maintenance requirement – the benefits of having no moving parts! But it was not until the global oil crisis of 1973 that development of terrestrial applications also became significant.

In parallel with developments for users in remote areas has been the provision of photovoltaic cells for low-power consumer goods, such as watches and calculators, where convenience is the key. Now there is a large range of areas in which photovoltaics offers a viable alternative to conventional means of power production.

Throughout the development of photovoltaics, efficiency has increased and cost has come down significantly. There are now many ground-based (or 'terrestrial') applications that are viable. Efficiencies of over 30% have been produced with exotic materials in the laboratory, and in production an efficiency of 15% is straightforward to achieve. There are perfectly satisfactory explanations of this rather low efficiency which we'll come to in due course.

Figure 2.1 Photovoltaic arrays on a satellite

without PV technology. PV technology provides a solution too in remote locations that are otherwise without power: galvanic protection of pipelines, radio-signal boosting, weather stations and power for isolated communities are all candidates for PV systems. A double benefit can be gained with mobile recharging systems for laptop computers, portable music systems and mobile phones, as *portable* equipment is here taken for use in *remote* locations. Large PV systems integrated into roofs or office buildings in urban environments and connected to the mains network have considerable appeal, but such concepts are better built-in from the start and most of our urban developments are not easily adaptable.

This part of Block 5 is an overview of photovoltaics: how it works, what materials are employed, and its likely place in the future scheme of energy generation and implementation.

The generation of useful electricity from sunlight is clearly a major engineering challenge. However, it should be examined in the overall context of power generation and the growing use of 'renewable' energy sources. This is the aim of the following section. I will then go on to look at just how sunlight can be used as an energy resource, before studying in more detail the technology and engineering of modern photovoltaic cells.

2 Photovoltaics in the context of renewable energy

Energy use is fundamental to our modern economy and society. Energy enables manufacturing, communications, transportation, entertainment and the domestic and work environments. However, its generation from nuclear and fossil fuels is presenting increasing problems (see ▼**Energy from atoms and molecules**▲). Long-term side effects, and limitations in the amount of fossil fuel available, mean that we must develop new attitudes to energy generation, and, therefore, perhaps new technologies for energy generation. Our future management of energy must be radically different from what took place in the twentieth century, unless we choose to return to a much simpler, less sophisticated society and economy. What is needed is an energy supply that is 'renewable'. In fact, the best we can hope for is something that appears on our timescales to be everlasting – rather like coal and oil must have looked a few generations ago. So, what we mean by 'renewable' is a resource that is naturally replenished over a short time span.

2.1 Types of renewable energy

The most widely used fuel in the world is biomass – wood and vegetation. In developing countries, wood is the most widely available fuel, especially in rural areas; but unfortunately for the most part it is not used in a renewable

---

▼Energy from atoms and molecules▲

There are a number of ways to get energy from atoms and molecules. Here are three. Burn a hydrocarbon or other organic substance; break up the nuclei of massive atoms; fuse together nuclei from some of the smaller atoms. The first is commonplace, but not without some environmental impact. The second is the nuclear industry's serious business. The third is incredibly difficult to control.

(i) Burning releases energy – things get hot as they burn. This is essentially a rapid process leading to chemical combination with oxygen; if the reaction is too rapid then an explosion is likely to occur.

A simple reaction to describe is the burning of carbon, the major component of coal, forming carbon dioxide.

$$C + O_2 \rightarrow CO_2$$

Two other simple reactions are the burning of hydrogen (making water) and the burning of methane, which we saw in Block 3 Part 4.

$$2H_2 + O_2 \rightarrow 2H_2O$$

$$CH_4 + 2O_2 \rightarrow CO_2 + 2H_2O$$

All we need here is to observe that rearranging the atoms in these reactions releases energy as heat. More complicated hydrocarbons such as fuel oil and aviation spirit burn in much the same way, giving the same energetically-preferred products (CO_2 and H_2O) together with lots of heat.

(ii) Very big atoms with nuclei that combine many tens of protons and neutrons are rarely stable,

energetically speaking. You know what happens to unstable systems – like a pencil balanced on its end, they are likely to fall into some more stable configuration which has lower energy. Some very big atoms emit radioactive particles as their nucleus shifts around to achieve some lower state of energy. Others, such as the type of uranium known as U235 (a huge atom with a total of 235 neutrons and protons in its nucleus), can be split apart by hitting them with neutrons – this is nuclear fission. Huge amounts of energy are released when such massive atoms are destroyed in this way. Nuclear power stations harness a substantial fraction of this energy released from nuclear fission – it amounts to 'taming' an atom bomb. An oft-quoted figure is that one tonne of uranium fuel can produce the same amount of electricity as 150 000 tonnes of coal.

(iii) At the other end of the nuclear scale are the tiny nuclei of hydrogen and helium atoms. Very small nuclei are also not favourable in energy terms, so considerable savings in energy can be made if small nuclei are squeezed together to make bigger nuclei, though enormous forces must be overcome before this can be achieved. This process is called nuclear fusion. Making a power station that recovers useful energy from nuclear fusion amounts to taming a hydrogen bomb and remains a dream of some researchers. Fusion processes in the Sun are responsible for its entire output of energy, demonstrating both the incredible potential of nuclear fusion and the extreme conditions associated with the ignition of fusion reactions.

fashion, resulting in deforestation. (This has further, knock-on effects, such as subsequent soil erosion, which can be a significant problem.) Properly managed biomass can be an important source of renewable energy. Several types of fast growing tree are suitable for short rotation coppicing, in which trees are harvested and replanted after about five years, in such a way as not to reduce the total number of growing trees. Other crops such as rapeseed and sugar cane are often grown for their oil, which has many uses, including fuel for transport. Sugar cane can also be converted into ethanol for use in motor vehicles.

Currently, the most widely implemented renewable energy scheme for large scale power generation is hydroelectricity, in which stored water is released downhill through generating turbines. Water gets into the high-level reservoir in two ways: either directly, after falling as rain or snow on higher ground; or there are also schemes where water is pumped from lower down when 'surplus' energy is available, to be released at times of peak energy demand. However, most suitable hydroelectric sites have now been developed, and there are significant social and ecological problems associated with forming the reservoirs. Also, suitable sites tend to be remote from areas requiring energy.

Tidal barrage schemes are similar to large scale hydro schemes, with the twice-daily tide carrying seawater into an adapted natural reservoir, which is drained via generating turbines. One such success, and a major engineering project, was the barrage across the estuary of the Rance just outside St Malo; see Figure 2.2. But the potential for large scale power generation in this way is not without major consequences for the environment, as large areas of land must be flooded to create the reservoir.

The smaller scale motion of the sea – wave power – may itself offer a useful way of generating electricity.

Windmills and watermills have long been used to provide mechanical energy from renewable sources. In many countries, wind farms in remote hilltop locations link mechanical energy through turbines to the electrical grid. However, wind energy is a highly variable resource, and no wind turbine will ever be able to provide power 100% of the time.

Figure 2.2 The Rance Tidal Barrage

This brings us on to solar power: energy from the Sun. Photovoltaics is the key to electricity generation directly from sunlight. As with wind power, though, the availability of solar energy is subject to variation, not just between night and day, but also as the length of day changes with the seasons, particularly at high latitudes. Solar power is also very dependent on the weather, although weather patterns are generally predictable over the longer term.

There are two technologies for harvesting solar energy. Solar thermal energy is used for space heating in passive designs of houses (e.g. just having south facing windows), and in systems where solar energy is used to heat the air within wall cavities, which is then actively circulated around the house. Alternatively, active solar water-heating with panels mounted on roofs will feed heated water either directly for use or via a heat exchanger for pre-heating domestic water; see Figure 2.3. There are also large-scale applications. Usually a series of mirrors is arranged to focus sunlight on a central tower, in which the heat is used to raise steam to drive turbines, generating electricity. These systems have to be big to minimize heat losses.

Figure 2.3 Roof-top solar thermal panel in Oxfordshire

Photovoltaic technology generates electricity directly from sunlight and is the main subject here. It is modular – i.e. it can be built up in small sections – and so is just as applicable to small scale domestic applications as to large power stations. Its chief benefits lie in its silent, pollution-free operation with almost zero maintenance, and it is well suited for use in urban environments, as compared to other options, such as wind power, because it takes up relatively little space. (A variant of the technology, thermo-photovoltaics, uses a particular type of photovoltaic cell to turn radiant energy from *any* heat source into electricity. The heat source can be from fossil fuels or biomass as well as from concentrated sunlight.)

Because of its variable nature, renewable energy usually requires integration with so-called 'power conditioning' – electrical engineering aimed at levelling the supply. This may involve energy-storage systems, such as batteries, or the hydro-storage mentioned earlier, or the use of the mains network as a store so that power is exported to the grid at times of abundance and imported at leaner times.

SAQ 2.1 (Learning outcomes 2.1 and 2.2)

(a) List four types of renewable energy.

(b) Give two advantages of photovoltaics compared to other renewable sources.

2.2 Why renewables?

For several decades the finite nature of fossil fuel reserves has been appreciated. Although known reserves have increased, this is offset by their greater inaccessibility. But there is another imperative for a reduced dependency on coal, gas and oil. Over the last two decades there has been mounting evidence, first for the increased level of pollutants and carbon dioxide in the atmosphere through the use of fossil fuels, and secondly that the increase in carbon dioxide is causing an increase in the temperature of the atmosphere through ▼The Greenhouse Effect▲. It is widely believed that this is having an effect on weather patterns and, consequently, sea level. The debate is now over how large and catastrophic these effects will be, and whether they can be reversed or at least mitigated.

Global temperatures have certainly risen over the past century by about 0.5 °C and the level of carbon dioxide (a major greenhouse gas) has increased from 280 ppm (parts per million) in pre-industrial times to a current level of 380 ppm (at the time of writing, 2001). Predictions for the rise in global temperatures over the next 100 years vary from 0.5 °C to 3 °C. The lower end of this scale will almost certainly be survivable, but even the smallest temperature increase may lead to more frequent and more catastrophic weather events. The Intergovernmental Panel for Climate Change has predicted that several low-lying Pacific islands will become swamped by increased sea levels as a result of ▼Seawater expansion▲ and that countries such as Bangladesh could lose as much as 17% of their land area – an area populated by around 20 million people. In addition to this, melting of the ice over Antarctica and Greenland will also have some effect on sea levels, but estimates of the extent to which such melting could increase sea levels, and thus the area of land that could potentially be flooded, vary widely and are inconclusive at the time of writing.

▼The Greenhouse Effect▲

Suppose you are uncomfortably warm and wish to feel cooler. What would you do? My guess is you are more likely to take off an item of clothing than to put one on. Of course, putting on another coat would lead to your becoming even warmer.

The greenhouse effect refers to the way in which temperatures rise when heat loss is inhibited, originally used in connection with glass 'greenhouses' used to provide a warm environment for plant growth. Such structures allow sunlight to pass through and fall upon objects within it. The warmed objects lose an equivalent amount of energy predominantly by emitting infrared radiation. Because the glass is less transparent to infrared than it is to sunlight, the insides warm up until they lose energy as fast as they gain it.

This effect is not restricted to greenhouses. It applies also to the entire global system. Radiation incident from the Sun warms the whole of the planet. The average temperature of the Earth is at a value that ensures that cooling by radiation emitted from the Earth's surface just balances the heating by radiation incident from the Sun. The atmosphere acts like the glass of the greenhouse. In particular, it is more difficult for radiation from the relatively cool surface of the Earth to penetrate the atmosphere than it is for radiation from the relatively hot surface of the Sun. In fact if this weren't the case and the Earth had no 'overcoat' provided by the atmosphere, then life as we know it would not exist – the entire surface would be frozen. In truth, when things are working as they should, the greenhouse effect is no bad thing.

The problem comes when, in effect, the Earth's overcoat is supplemented by another layer or a more effective material...in these terms I would expect to be hotter in two overcoats than I am inside one. For the Earth, gases such as carbon dioxide and water vapour are responsible for ensuring that the atmosphere acts as this overcoat. So we have to be careful. Increased levels of carbon dioxide in the atmosphere resulting from the burning of fossil fuels causes an enhancing of the greenhouse effect.

▼Seawater expansion▲

Water does not expand much on heating: a mere 0.02% per degree Celsius. That's not much; surely it can't lead to significant deepening of warmed oceans? So what if the top few metres of water do become a little warmer?

Let's try a few sums. To keep things simple I'll presume that sideways expansion is restricted by the continental land masses so that any expansion of the water in the sea causes a simple increase in its depth, see Figure 2.4.

The US National Oceanic and Atmospheric Administration have examined seawater temperatures over forty years towards the end of the twentieth century and reported the following:

■ A temperature rise of about 0.3 degrees Celsius on average over the first 300 m of depth has occurred.

■ A temperature rise of about 0.06 degrees Celsius on average over the range from 300 to 3000 m of depth has also occurred.

The depth of water expands by 0.02% per degree Celsius. That's 0.2 mm per metre of depth for each degree Celsius. For the first 300 m the expansion is (0.2×300) mm per degree Celsius, so a 0.3 degree Celsius rise would cause a depth increase of

$$0.3 \times (0.2 \times 300) \text{ mm} = 18 \text{ mm}.$$

The next 2700 m will similarly account for an extra depth of over half as much again.

> **Exercise 2.1**
>
> Show that expansion of 2700 m of deep sea on warming by a mere 0.06 degrees Celsius will lead to a depth increase of about 30 mm.

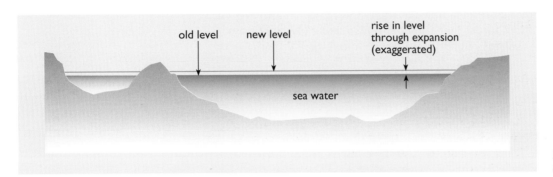

Figure 2.4 Seawater expansion

Hence, there are compelling reasons to rapidly expand energy generation technologies that are non-polluting. The facts are becoming recognized at an international level. The first climate change conference at Rio de Janeiro in 1992, followed by the conference at Kyoto in 1997, sought to set legally binding commitments on countries for reductions in carbon dioxide emissions so as to achieve the same levels of emission as existed in 1990. As a result of this there are two targets to which the UK is now committed. These are to reduce carbon dioxide emissions by 12.5% of their 1990-level by 2010, and the more general goal of cutting total greenhouse gas emissions by 20% of their 1990-level by the same year. Measures to achieve this include cleaning up factory and power station emissions, reducing energy consumption and increasing energy generation from renewable energy sources. This last has been translated into an increase in renewable energy generation to a level of 10% by 2020, from a level in 2000 of about 1%.

Against this background renewable energy based on the Sun appears a promising option. Approximately the same amount of energy falls on the Earth's surface in one hour as the whole of human civilization uses in a whole year. Although most of this falls on the sea and relatively inaccessible land areas, and of course drives the weather and other global processes, there is still a vast store to be tapped, for which we are now developing the technology.

> **SAQ 2.2** (Learning outcome 2.1)
>
> List the main problems associated with continued and increasing use of fossil fuels.

2.3 Why photovoltaics?

Electricity is the most versatile form of energy available to us, and is intimately integrated into our society. It can be generated from many sources, can readily be distributed, and can be used for almost any application. For example, high-quality lighting, motors for machines and appliances, communications and entertainment equipment are all readily fuelled by electricity. It is also used for heating and cooking and even for transport.

Renewable energy systems that generate electricity directly are particularly appropriate for integration into our existing infrastructure. These systems include hydro-, tidal-, wave- and wind-power and photovoltaics (PV). The first three of these, hydro, tidal and wave, are necessarily large systems, and are also very dependent on location. Wind farms produce electricity directly and can be sited close to points of use, but they are not suitable for the urban environment. Furthermore, the efficiency of wind turbines increases with size because wind speed increases with height. By their very nature wind turbines have to be obtrusive.

PV technology stands out as the only renewable option that generates electricity directly, is suitable for both small- and large-scale applications and the urban environment and remote applications alike, is silent and is a very low maintenance ('fit and forget') technology. It also has a low 'embodied energy', meaning the amount of energy invested in making PV modules is relatively small. It is generally recognized that PV is the most versatile of the renewable energy technologies and the most likely to be integrated on the small to medium scale. We need to know ▼Where the Sun shines brightly▲.

2.4 PV terminology

Figure 2.6 explains some of the terminology applied to photovoltaics. The photovoltaic or solar cell is the base unit. In Section 3 of this part we will look at the way the cell works, and in Section 4 we will look at the way cells are manufactured and the materials from which they are made.

Cells are connected together electrically and fabricated into modules, and these are installed at a site in an arrangement known as an array. There remains the task of conditioning the d.c. electricity from the array. This may

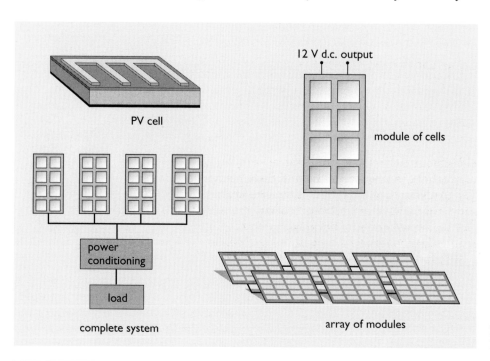

Figure 2.6 Photovoltaic hierarchy

▼Where the Sun shines brightly▲

Solar energy is highly seasonal and variable. Figure 2.5 gives an idea of its variation through the year in four locations. These are averages over a month and take into account typical weather.

The amount of sunlight reaching a given location on average in a given month can be predicted from past records with a fair degree of accuracy. This sunlight includes direct sunshine and the diffuse daylight that occurs on overcast days. Although not transmitting as much energy, this latter component can add a significant fraction to the overall energy levels, particularly in a temperate climate such as that in the UK. Another factor is that at relatively high latitudes, such as the UK, the length of the days in summer means that the total amount of energy compares quite well with those countries where the Sun is higher in the sky. Of course this advantage is reversed in the winter.

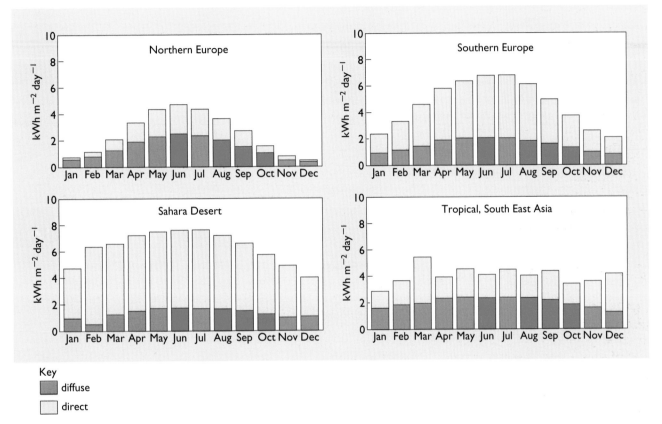

Key
- ▓ diffuse
- ☐ direct

Figure 2.5 Solar radiation at various places throughout the year

involve storage in batteries, or conversion to a.c. which may then be connected to the mains. These factors are discussed further in Section 5.2.

2.5 Summary

Renewable energy, together with energy consumption reduction and greater energy efficiency, offer a route to offset the consequences of climate change which are occurring through the over-use of fossil fuels. There are many resources and technologies, but for electricity generation in urban and remote environments alike, photovoltaics may be the best option because of its modularity and quiet, maintenance-free operation. The technology is also suitable for integration with existing fossil fuel resources, or with other renewables, to overcome the mismatch between resource availability and demand.

3 Photovoltaics – making light work

A century and a half after the interesting observation that light can interact electrically with certain materials, enough is understood to explain how this interaction occurs; and further, to understand what must be done to construct efficient photovoltaic cells. The task calls for processes by which the energy of light can be captured, and can be used to separate electrical charge, just as chemical energy is required to do in a battery. At the heart of the story are the semiconductor materials of the electronics world, but the nature of light itself is where we must begin.

3.1 Sunlight: the resource to be harvested

Before investigating how to exploit a resource, it pays to develop an appreciation for what the resource is. Just how much energy is available in sunlight day-by-day, and what form is the energy in?

Any electromagnetic radiation, such as light from the Sun, comes in a stream of discrete bundles of energy known as photons. There is a wide, continuous range of possible sizes for such a bundle of energy. In discussing light we restrict ourselves to considering the part of the electromagnetic spectrum incorporating the so-called visible spectrum and the adjacent regions known as the ultraviolet (UV) and infrared (IR); see Figure 2.7.

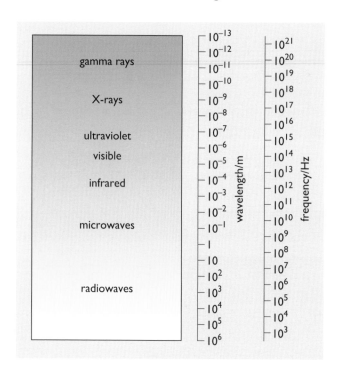

Figure 2.7 The electromagnetic spectrum

There is a correspondence between the energy of a photon and the wavelength of light. The wavelengths associated with light span from 0.1 μm (10^{-7} m, UV) to over 100 μm (10^{-4} m, IR) and the energy associated with a given wavelength is given by the following expression.

$$E \text{ (in joules)} = 2.0 \times 10^{-25}/\lambda \text{ (in metres)}$$

Here the number 2.0×10^{-25} is a constant – but there are, of course, some units wrapped up in the conversion factor: this is just a simple equation that converts from wavelength to energy.

The bundles of energy are rather small, typically of the order of 10^{-19} joules, and a more convenient unit is found in practice by dividing the energy by the charge of an electron (1.6×10^{-19} coulombs, where the 'coulomb' is a unit for electric charge – more on this later) to give a quantity known as an electron volt or eV (said 'ee-vee'). The electron volt is actually a unit of energy. Don't worry too much about the details of this; for our purposes it's just a way of making the numbers easier to follow. The electron volt is often used as a convenient unit for energy at the atomic scale. So it turns out that

E (in eV) = $1.24/\lambda$ (in μm)

The energy of photons of light falls within the range 12.4 eV (UV) to 0.124 eV (IR).

Exercise 2.2

Calculate the energy in eV of photons associated with blue-ish light that has a wavelength of 0.50 μm, green-ish light at 0.55 μm and red-ish light at 0.64 μm.

What makes one source of light appear different from another are the relative amounts of photons of different energy that each source contains. Figure 2.8(a) shows a 'white light' spectrum – one that contains roughly equal contributions from all energies; to our eyes it would in fact appear a flat white. Adding more contribution from the blue, higher-energy end tends to give us the feeling of a 'colder' white, but this is an emotional response and has nothing to do with the energy of the photons involved.

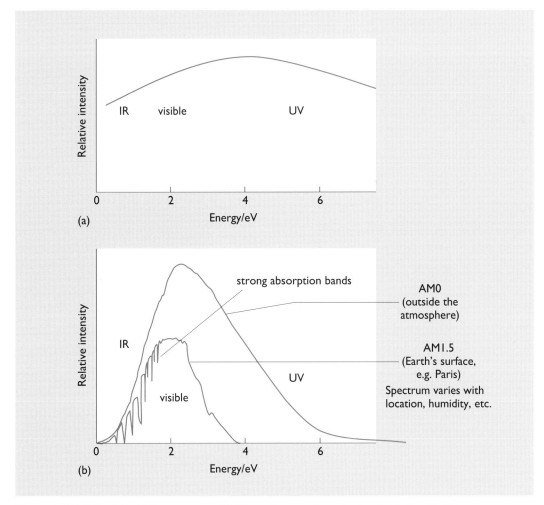

Figure 2.8 (a) A white light spectrum (b) The solar spectrum just outside the Earth's atmosphere and at the Earth's surface near the latitude of Paris

The spectrum of solar photons is shown in Figure 2.8(b) as measured at two places: above the atmosphere and on the ground. Apart from occasional periods of high activity on the Sun, the solar spectrum above the atmosphere is reasonably constant at present, and has been for about 4 billion years, and is set to be so for at least another 5 billion years; the spectrum on the ground is affected by local factors such as humidity.

The Sun's spectrum just outside the Earth's atmosphere is known as the 'air mass zero' condition (or AM0) because it corresponds to the range of solar energy before it passes through the atmosphere. Figure 2.8(b) shows that the passage through the atmosphere has two effects on the solar spectrum – what are they?

The first is an overall loss – there is simply less light; it turns out that a large fraction of the light is scattered from its straight line path by the atmosphere. The second is loss in specific bands on the lower energy branch of the spectrum; certain energies are apparently absorbed before they penetrate to ground level. It's worth finding out a bit more about these: see ▼Atmospheric effects▲.

▼Atmospheric effects▲

Did you ever wonder why a bright cloudy sky is white and a cloudless sky is blue? Read on, but watch out for technical terms related to scattering and absorption. Let's start with a little light refreshment.

Espresso coffee has a whitish froth over inky black liquid. Stout beer is served with a generous whitish froth formed of the dark beer. The dark appearance in both cases arises because the liquids *absorb* light so strongly that most of the light that is directed as if to pass through it penetrates only a few millimetres. The liquids contain matter that readily takes up energy from the light. By contrast, the froths are mostly air and not liquid. They are made up of masses of tiny air bubbles, virtually miniature balloons formed from very thin skins of liquid. Each bubble acts like a tiny lens. Rays of light encountering froth are *scattered* through different angles depending on where they enter a bubble; see Figure 2.9. As a result the froths diffusely reflect white light before any significant thickness of liquid can absorb it. You can probably see the link to clouds, but the blue sky bit is more subtle.

Clouds are made up of tiny droplets of water. Each droplet acts like a tiny lens. Rays of sunlight encountering a cloud are scattered through different angles depending on where they enter a droplet. As a result clouds *scatter* white light. Sunlight is said to be diffused (i.e. scattered) by clouds so that light from the bright disk of the Sun is spread across the cloud; scattering redistributes light in all directions so that a major fraction of energy racing along rays of sunlight is diverted by clouds before it reaches the ground – some goes back into space, some goes sideways and some still goes forwards, though no longer in sharply defined rays.

Clouds of water droplets are not the only component of the atmosphere that can scatter light. Smaller still are microscopic dust particles and the molecules in the air itself. These scatter light even on a clear day and it turns out that such small objects tend to scatter the blue end of the spectrum over ten times more than they scatter the

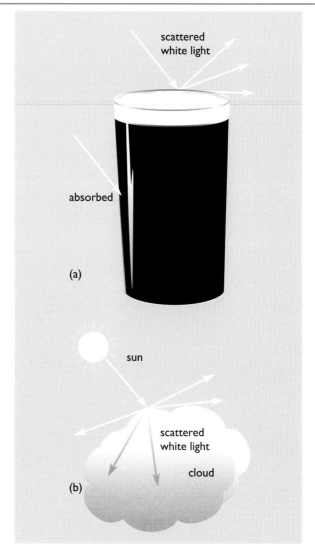

Figure 2.9 Light absorption and scattering (a) by a frothy drink and (b) by a cloud

red end. Look up on a clear day and you don't see the darkness of outer space; what you see is light that was passing overhead until it got scattered. Red light is only weakly scattered and ten times as much blue light reaches your eyes, so what you see is predominantly blue. Similarly, light from a setting or rising sun takes a long, grazing path through the atmosphere (almost one hundred times longer than the shortest way through) so that such light reaching the Earth has had all its blueness scattered out. Thus the Sun's disk appears reddish.

There is also a lot of absorption of the solar radiation by molecules in the atmosphere. This occurs at specific wavelengths depending on the molecules involved, as shown by the bands in Figure 2.8. In the upper atmosphere, highly reactive ozone absorbs very short wavelength ultraviolet, though not all of it – some does still get through. Lower in the atmosphere the predominant absorbing molecules are water and carbon dioxide. The greatest effect on the amount of sunlight reaching the surface is that caused by absorption by water vapour. Carbon dioxide mostly affects the infrared part of the spectrum, which is not a very large component of sunlight. However, carbon dioxide *is* very important for warming of the atmosphere by re-radiated energy from the ground – The Greenhouse Effect.

Scattering, reflection and absorption effects result, on average, in at least a 30% attenuation of the direct sunlight that reaches the ground.

The accepted average figure for the total rate of energy flux or power density, at AM0, from the sum of all the photons incident, is 1360 W m^{-2} (i.e. 1360 joules of energy every second per square metre). This is known as the solar constant, and it is indeed fairly constant over the course of a year.

The most important single factor that determines the total power of sunlight reaching the ground is the thickness of atmosphere it has to pass through. For any point on the surface, the path from the Sun through the atmosphere to that point is at a minimum when the Sun is directly overhead – that is, at its zenith. This condition is known as 'air mass one' (or AM1) so that other paths can be compared with it. As you can guess, the resulting spectrum at ground level is a much less constant quantity than AM0, being greatly affected by weather and air quality. The generally accepted figure for AM1 is a total incident power density of about 1000 W m^{-2}.

For a point on the surface where the Sun is not directly overhead, there is a greater amount of air for the light to pass through, because the path through the atmosphere is longer. The total incident power density is accordingly less than at the point on the globe where it is overhead.

Figure 2.10 sets up the geometrical picture. It turns out that the relative length of the path is related to the cosine of an angle (Block 3 Part 2). If the angle the Sun makes to the vertical is θ ('theta'), then the length of the path compared

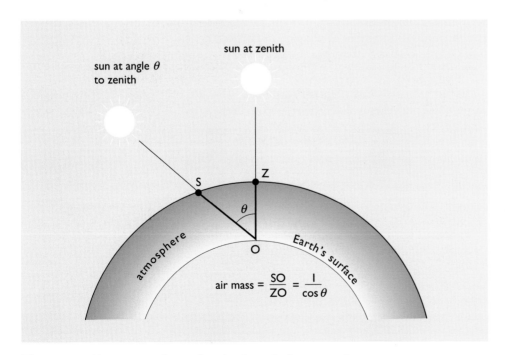

Figure 2.10 Air mass number and paths through the atmosphere

with that when the Sun is directly overhead is 1/cos (θ). The numerical value of 1/cos (θ) for a particular angle of sunlight gives a measure of the path length relative to the perpendicular route associated with AM1. In other words, the numerical value of 1/cos (θ) is a relative measure of the amount of air, or air mass, in the path, so it is used to define the air mass number.

Exercise 2.3

For $\theta = 60°$, $\cos(\theta) = \frac{1}{2}$

Calculate the air mass number for sunlight entering the atmosphere at 60°.

The actual air mass between you and the Sun at any time also depends on the time of day, the season of the year and the angle of latitude. In order to make meaningful comparisons of solar cells, an internationally agreed standard air mass of AM 1.5 is used in recording performance. This corresponds to solar noon (meaning the time when the Sun is at its highest point in the sky) at a latitude of 48° (approximately the equivalent of Paris on the spring or autumn equinox – the times of the year when the day and night are of equal length), in clear weather with low humidity.

Look again at Figure 2.8(b). A large fraction of the higher energy (shorter wavelength) ultraviolet radiation is filtered out by the atmosphere, predominantly by the ozone layer. The attenuation at lower energy, the red end, is restricted to a few specific, but rather strong, bands of absorption.

The power of sunlight is further reduced for a different reason when the Sun is not directly overhead. Imagine a window frame 1 m × 1 m, held so that the Sun's rays pass through it perpendicularly. See Figure 2.11. Near the equator at midday I'd have to hold the window over my head to achieve this. The patch of ground illuminated within the frame would be about 1 m × 1 m. But in the UK in the middle of winter I'd have to hold the frame almost upright, because the Sun would be very low in the sky. The ground area illuminated in this case would be a long rectangle 1 m wide. The length of the rectangle depends on the angle between the Sun and the vertical. Illumination that would be 1 kW m^{-2} at the equator gets smeared out as latitude increases, so that at a latitude of 48° (e.g. Paris) the illuminated rectangle would have dimensions of 1 m × 1.5 m, reducing the strength of illumination geometrically to only 0.62 kW m^{-2}. Clearly it would be worthwhile tilting any receiver to offset this effect. The same considerations apply to the changes in the apparent strength of the Sun with the time of day. Perhaps a sophisticated system for harvesting sunlight should track the Sun across the sky hour by hour?

This introduces a further factor to the internationally agreed standard – the standard spectrum used to compare the performance of photovoltaic devices is the spectrum at AM1.5, *scaled up to give a total incident power of exactly 1 kW m^{-2}*. This is the best way to deal with the variability of sunlight caused by factors such as those described above, and it makes calculations easier, but it does put a rather optimistic gloss on the results.

SAQ 2.3 (Learning outcomes 2.3, 2.4 and 2.11)

(a) Considering the illuminated area of the Earth to be a circle with radius 3600 km (the radius of the Earth), estimate the total power of the sunlight falling on the Earth.

(b) Spread the power calculated in part (a) over the entire (both light and dark areas) surface of the Earth to deduce a rough figure for the power density in W m^{-2}. The surface area of a sphere is $4\pi r^2$, where r is the radius of the sphere.

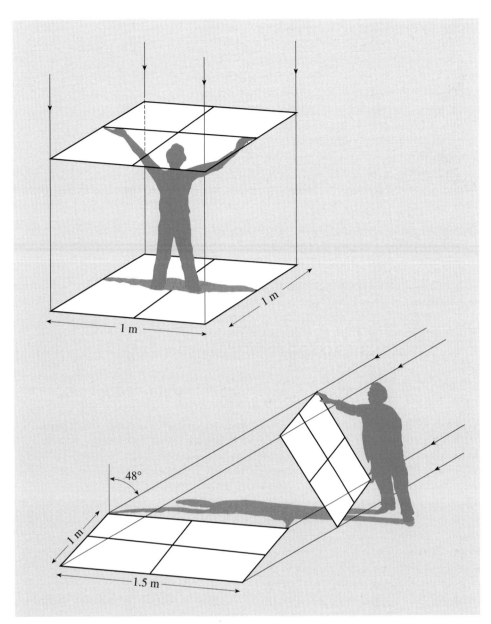

Figure 2.11 The 'shadow' of a window

SAQ 2.4 (Learning outcomes 2.3 and 2.4)

Explain why the peak solar power on midsummer's day at solar noon in London (latitude 52°) will be less than that in the northern tropics (around latitude 22°), also at solar noon; include an estimate of the effective air mass number for London at the given time.

SAQ 2.5 (Learning outcomes 2.4 and 2.11)

Solar powered calculators use low efficiency solar cells (about 5% efficient). They work in diffuse daylight or even artificial light, which has a much lower power density (about 25 W m^{-2}) than direct sunlight (nominally 1000 W m^{-2}). However, because they use liquid crystal displays and low power electronics, their power requirement is also very low (about 0.5 mW).

Using these figures, calculate the cell area required to power a calculator.

SAQ 2.6 (Learning outcomes 2.4 and 2.11)

From the data in Figure 2.5 propose a rule-of-thumb value for the effective energy in *diffuse* sunlight, per square metre per day, averaged over a year, that could be expected in London.

3.2 Passing energy from photons to electrons

The important point to know about any photon is that its energy bundle is indivisible – it is a fixed quantity, or 'quantum', of energy. A photon can be absorbed by matter only as a whole lump; there is no such thing as 'half a photon'. It is equally true to say that matter can only absorb photons of particular energies; that is, the absorption process is selective to which photons can participate.

Exercise 2.4

It is useful to have some idea of how many photons per second strike each square metre of ground under the standard AM1.5 specification of 1000 W m^{-2}.

Estimate the effective photon flux (number of photons per square metre per second), taking the average energy of each photon to be 2 eV, which is $2 \times (1.6 \times 10^{-19})$ joules.

Check your result with the given answer and write it below for future reference:

AM1.5 at 1000 W m^{-2} is equivalent to .... photons m^{-2} s^{-1}.

In the atmosphere, absorption of low energy photons occurs when the molecules present as gases (or liquid droplets) offer opportunities for photons of specific energy to be absorbed. The energy is transferred into vibrations

---

▼Solar-heated water panels▲

Bad news for solar-heated water panels: the absorption of photon energy by water molecules is restricted to only a few low energy bands and the atmosphere has already had a go at these. If you want to heat water using energy from sunlight you'll need first to turn the radiant solar energy into thermal energy. Blackened surfaces do this very effectively, as you will have noticed if you've had to touch anything in a closed motor car during a sunny day. The blackened surface absorbs a wide range of photon energies...that's why it appears black. The construction of a typical solar-heated water panel is shown in Figure 2.12.

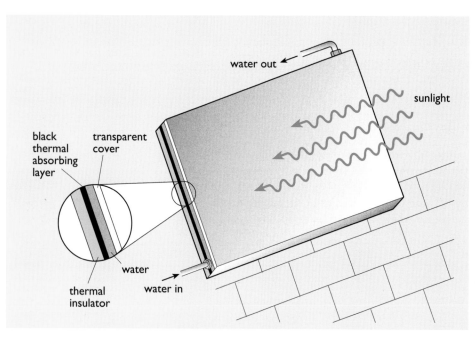

Figure 2.12 Construction of a typical solar-heated water panel

within the molecules. Vibrating molecules are effectively 'hot' molecules. The bundles of energy associated with these vibrations are relatively small, so molecules predominantly absorb low energy (infrared) photons. There is clear evidence of this in Figure 2.8(b), where the atmospheric absorption between 1–1.5 eV is largely due to water molecules. This is also the process by which ▼Solar-heated water panels▲ extract energy from sunlight, and it accounts for why anything left in sunlight tends to get hot.

If different types of matter can absorb photons of specific energies only, then it is worth asking whether there are any substances particularly suited to absorbing the higher energy, visible, photons around the peak of the AM1.5 spectrum in Figure 2.8(b). Such substances would be useful, wouldn't they?

By chance (or good design on a cosmic scale), there is a range of materials that are naturally close to our needs. These are ▼Semiconductors▲ and they are certainly worth a closer look to see how their behaviour can be engineered to our advantage. What makes them even more interesting is that the way in which they absorb light is intimately linked with their electrical properties. That is the key to turning light into electricity.

3.2.1 The photoconductivity of semiconductors

When a source of e.m.f. (e.g. a battery) is connected across a piece of semiconductor, current flows in proportion to the voltage. That should sound familiar – didn't Ohm say as much in describing resistance? He did, though he wasn't working with semiconductors. If he had been, he'd have been able

---

▼Semiconductors▲

We met semiconductors in Block 4 Part 3; as their name suggests, the electrical conductivity of semiconductors lies between that of insulators and conductors. Suppose you have some short rods composed of typical examples of each class of material: say copper, silicon and porcelain. The copper sample would be over a million times more conducting than the silicon. The silicon would in turn be several million times more conducting than the porcelain. What's needed for electrical conduction is lots of easily moved electrons within the structure of the material. Clearly, porcelain is such a poor conductor because it has few of these. Silicon, however, has a small number of very mobile electrons. Copper has so many easily moved electrons that they actually tend to get in each other's way!

There are two key differences between semiconductors and ordinary, metallic conductors. First, the extent to which pure semiconductors conduct electricity is enormously sensitive to temperature. Second, the extent to which semiconductors conduct electricity is enormously sensitive to impurity content. Why?

To answer this we have to look at examples of semiconducting materials. Silicon (Si) and germanium (Ge) are typical. Their atoms form bonds amongst themselves by sharing four of their electrons with four neighbours (this sharing of electrons leads to so-called 'covalent' bonds). They build up a three-dimensional crystal with each atom surrounded by, and bonded to, four others. A simple *two-dimensional* picture of this is sketched in Figure 2.13.

The bonds that hold the atoms together also hold the electrons in place. What defines a semiconductor is that a

relatively small amount of energy – such as room temperature heat – can break some bonds and thus free some electrons. Once they have escaped their bonds electrons are free to wander around the structure. Hence, the higher the temperature the greater the number of bonds broken, the more free electrons, and so the higher is the conductivity. That accounts for the first characteristic property; see Figure 2.13(b).

When a bond is broken and an electron becomes mobile, it leaves behind it a lack of an electron – a hole. These holes are very important in semiconductors because they act just like positive charge carriers, as the hole can be passed from atom to atom like a sort of 'I-owe-you (IOU) an electron'. Holes add another mechanism for conducting electricity, as they provide a path for electrons to move.

Another way to free an electron in a semiconductor structure is associated with impurity atoms. Any impurity atom that tries to sit where a silicon atom should be ought to offer four electrons for sharing in the formation of bonds. Now, suppose an impurity (e.g. phosphorus) arrives with five electrons to share. Four immediately have places to go but the fifth is, so to speak, homeless. The extra electron is able to wander off just like one of those that has been thermally liberated. That accounts for the second characteristic property; see Figure 2.13 (c).

Exercise 2.5 Freeing holes

Identify the characteristic property that an impurity must have if it is to introduce a hole (that is 'IOU an electron') into a crystal of silicon. See Figure 2.13(c).

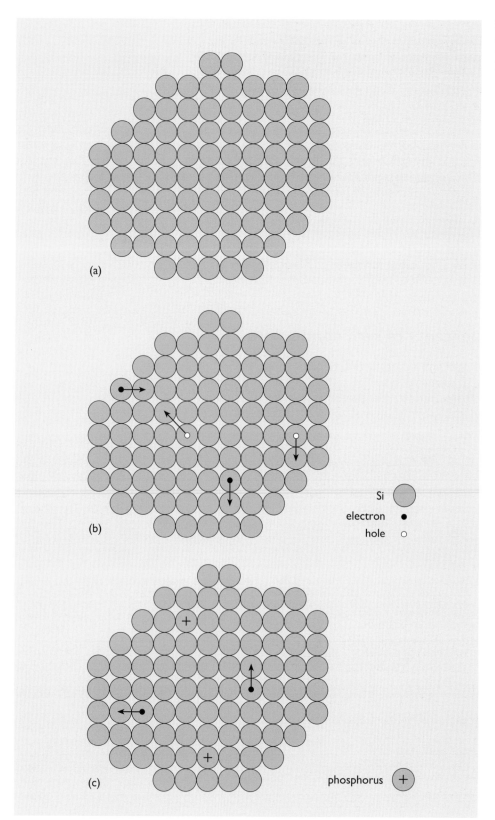

Figure 2.13 Semiconducting materials: (a) very cold and pure (b) warm and pure (c) cold and less pure

Si ⬤ (grey circle)

electron ●

hole ○

phosphorus ⊕

to observe that in a thin slice of silicon, say, for a given voltage more current would flow on brighter days than on dull ones and that currents were always much feebler at night. See Figure 2.14. Apparently, pure semiconductors are better conductors in stronger light. That is, their electrical conductivity is somehow enhanced by the arrival on their surface of photons. This is an effect called photoconductivity.

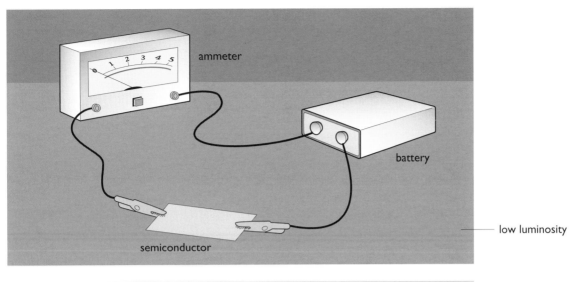

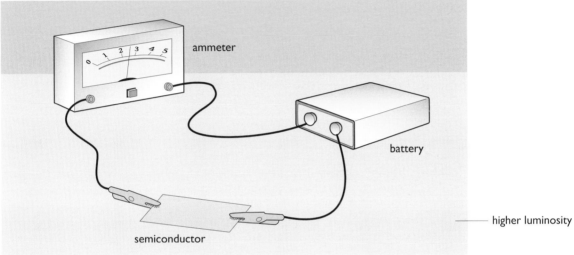

Figure 2.14 A photoconductivity experiment

So, conductivity in a material is due to the presence of free charge carriers, usually electrons (though ions, when free to move, can also contribute, as we saw in connection with batteries). The extra conductivity that photons can induce in a semiconductor comes from the freeing of extra charge carriers by providing energy through the absorption of photons. The energy of the photon goes into springing an electron from the atom it's bonded to, leaving it free to roam around the material; we'll come back to the hole it leaves behind. It turns out that there is a minimum, or threshold, energy that the photon must have to liberate an electron in such a way; different materials have different thresholds.

Before we go further into the curious properties of semiconducting materials we need to recall briefly how matter interacts with photons. I'll do so in three steps.

First, isolated atoms are very selective about which energies can be absorbed; only photons with particular precise values of energy are acceptable. It's to do with the way atoms hold electrons in very precisely defined orbits or 'energy levels' – a specific amount of energy is required for the electrons to climb out of their orbit.

Second, small molecules are a little less fussy, but still will only accept a narrow range of energy around very particular values. The precise values are again a result of how the electrons are held; there is a slight blurring in the precision because some electrons are shared by more than one atom.

Third, the large agglomerations of atoms in solids are apparently still selective at the bottom end, having a clearly defined threshold energy, but beyond the threshold it turns out that photons with energies anywhere in a wide range can be absorbed. In semiconductors every atom shares electrons with several of its neighbours in such a way that the precise selectivity of the isolated atoms is smeared out above the threshold; furthermore, the threshold energy in semiconductors corresponds closely to the visible spectrum.

That's the way Nature made it. Physicists have a pretty convincing explanation of it all in which they speak of a 'band gap' rather than a 'threshold energy', but we don't need the details. What we do need is some idea of the threshold energies of some of these semiconductors for comparison with the spectrum in Figure 2.8(b).

Exercise 2.6

Mark on Figure 2.8(b) the threshold energies for the three semiconductor materials in Table 2.1, and so identify the material best matched to sunlight.

Table 2.1 Threshold energies for a range of semiconducting materials

Material	Threshold energy/eV
Germanium, Ge	0.61
Silicon, Si	1.12
Cadmium sulphide, CdS	2.42

It is very important to realize that the photosensitivity of semiconductors is subject to a threshold in energy. For instance, no amount of infrared photons, nor photons with energies in the red, yellow and green parts of the visible spectrum (below 2.42 eV) can affect the conductivity of cadmium sulphide. On the other hand, provided the photons are beyond the threshold, the enhancement to conductivity scales directly with the number of photons on offer. (I have noticed an equivalent effect when trying to exchange foreign money at a bureau de change – if I have $400 in coins, such as cents, nickels, dimes and quarters, the bureau de change simply won't accept it in such small lumps. Nothing less than the dollar bill is tradeable.)

Photoconductivity is a useful phenomenon for photographers. The light meter in many film cameras uses the resistance of a thin strip of the semiconductor cadmium sulphide (CdS) as a sensitive indicator of the amount of light; see Figure 2.15. The resistance falls in proportion to the illumination so you, or the electronic controller, can work out how to set the shutter speed. The shutter need only be open for a short time if there is lots of light, and this condition would be detected by the relatively low resistance of the CdS specimen. Lesser light levels would lead to higher resistance of the detector, whereupon shutter times need to be longer.

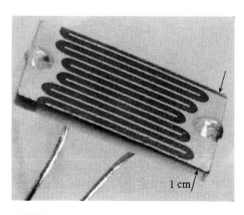

1 cm

Figure 2.15 A cadmium sulphide photocell. Current flows between the interdigitated combs (the lighter regions) crossing the cadmium sulphide (darker) material the short way

Exercise 2.7

According to the previous exercise germanium is an excellent photoconductor. Suggest one reason why neither it nor silicon are used in the light meter of a film camera.

3.2.2 Manipulating the conductivity of semiconductors

Semiconductors can certainly do the first part of what is required for a photovoltaic system: they capture photons, transferring energy into some of the host's electrons and freeing them from their parent atoms. Photoconductivity is all very well, but it is not *generating* electricity in the sense that it will drive current through a material; it simply affects the ease with which some external source of e.m.f. such as a battery can drive a current through a material. To *generate* electricity we need some way of separating electrical charge, so we can divert it into an external circuit. We saw in Part 1 of this block how in a battery chemical energy is used to do this.

The next step becomes clearer if we pause to think what will happen when the stream of photons falling on a semiconductor is suddenly cut off. Eventually, any hole vacated by the freeing of an electron will recapture an electron and the energy 'borrowed' in the escape is passed on somewhere else, usually as heat. The recombination of an electron with a hole is in fact completed in a tiny fraction of a second after the light goes out. Of course, it is going on all the time while the light is on too, but the continued absorption of photons generates new electron–hole pairs all the time. Things remain steady when the birth rate (generation by photons) equals the death rate (recombination) – you've seen this idea of things building up until a steady state is established before (for example, in connection with the operating temperature of a PC in Block 3 Part 4). To make a photovoltaic device, we'll need to find a way of preventing this rapid recombination, so we can divert the freed charge into an external circuit.

What electronic engineers do with semiconductors is to control the conductivity by adding tiny, measured amounts of impurities: they talk about ▼Doping semiconductors▲. By adding dopants the conductivity of a semiconductor can be precisely controlled. One class of dopant launches freed electrons while another class of dopant traps electrons, effectively launching the second type of charge carrier, the ones known as holes. The fun really starts when different parts of the same piece of semiconductor are given different dopants.

▼Doping semiconductors▲

Silicon is the most widely used semiconductor. We have more knowledge and experience of using this than any other semiconductor. Silicon is very abundant in ordinary sand (as 'silica' – silicon dioxide) and is used extensively in the electronics industry. It is also the most commonly used material for solar cells. Many other materials are also semiconductors; the discussion here is about silicon but equivalent doping effects arise in all semiconductors.

I suggested earlier that impurity atoms in a lump of silicon could free charge carriers, to the benefit of conductivity. 'Doping' is the technical term for doing this deliberately. You start with pure silicon and then you introduce a controlled amount of selected impurity.

To distinguish a deliberate addition from residual impurity it is termed a 'dopant'. But just how can you place dopant atoms into a lump of silicon?

Could it be as easy as melting the silicon and stirring in the dopant before re-solidifying? Well, yes and no. That would work, but more imaginative schemes have been evolved to cope with the demands of the electronics industry where different dopants are required to be carefully placed in different parts of very pure silicon. This is done by heating silicon to a little below its melting point in an atmosphere of dopant. The dopant atoms slowly diffuse into the heated solid at the rate of around a millionth of a metre per hour. See Figure 2.16.

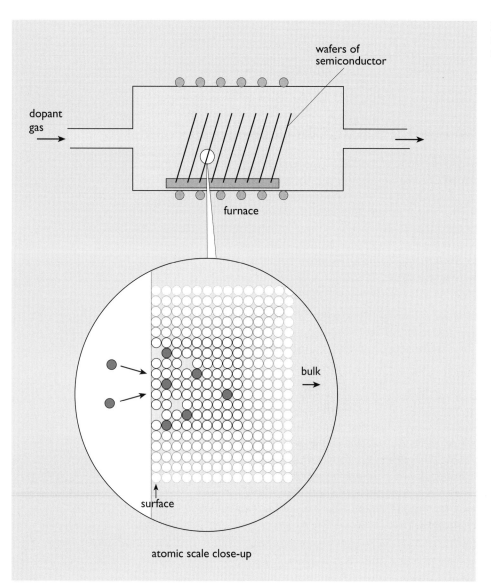

Figure 2.16 Introducing a dopant to generate freed electrons and holes

wafers of
semiconductor

dopant
gas

furnace

bulk

surface

atomic scale close-up

As a result of doping, a few host atoms are replaced with impurity atoms. Phosphorus atoms are ideal for launching freed electrons into silicon as they have five electrons available for bonding with other atoms, of which only four are required for the phosphorus to fit into the silicon's structure. Each phosphorus atom donates a spare electron. Material doped with phosphorus is known as *n-type* because the charge carriers it launches are negative (electrons). Various other dopants will have a similar effect.

A different class of dopant generates holes. In this case there is a 'shortage' of one electron, which creates a 'hole'. Holes behave as if they are positive charges. Electrons can jump into a hole, so the hole appears to 'move' in the opposite direction to the electron motion. Material that has been doped so as to launch holes is known as *p-type*, because effectively the holes act as positive charge carriers.

3.2.3 A p–n junction

Suppose the top half of a thin slice of silicon is doped to launch lots of freed electrons (n-type semiconductor) and that the lower half has been doped to launch lots of holes (p-type semiconductor). What happens in the middle?

In the middle there is a region between the two different types of semiconductor, where electrons from the upper half have recombined with holes from the lower half. The region is called a p–n junction, for obvious reasons.

Each freed electron in the upper (n-type) half is notionally paired with one of the dopant atoms present among the other atoms of the material. Likewise, holes in the lower half (p-type) are partnered by their parent dopant atom.

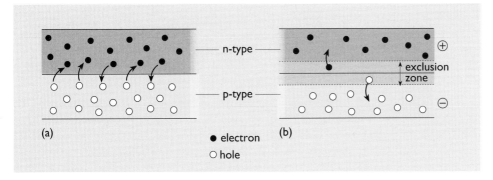

Figure 2.17 Development of a p–n junction: (a) electrons and holes spill out from their respective halves and begin to recombine; (b) after a time an electric force develops, which discourages charges from moving out of the section that they originated from

If the recombination across the junction were to go on unchecked, the top half would empty all its electrons into holes in the bottom half, leaving the upper half short of electrons and positively charged; the lower half would end up negatively charged by the arrival of the electrons. The process begins as described, but as it spreads back from the middle the build up of charge becomes important. The top half, becoming positively charged, pulls its wandering electrons back from the edge, preventing them from approaching the lower half where most of the holes are; see Figure 2.17(b). Similarly, holes are held back in their half. Pulling on charges like this is done through an 'electric field' that acts on charge like a gravitational field acts on mass.

Between the different types of semiconductor a zone with strong fields is established, thus keeping the electrons and holes in their respective halves. This is often referred to as a 'depletion region' as the free charges are somewhat depleted in number as a result; it's such a severe depletion here that I'm going to call it the 'exclusion zone'. We were looking for a way of separating charge and it looks like we've got an effective one here; the electrical forces that maintain the exclusion zone push negative charge one way and positive charge the other way. What happens if we shine light on this lot?

There are two situations to consider – the material outside the exclusion zone and that lying within it.

Away from the exclusion zone the photons beyond the threshold energy are absorbed, generating electron–hole pairs in much the same way as in the pure material discussed earlier, except that the increase in conductivity is considerably smaller. This lower level of conductivity occurs because, in the region with lots of electrons already freed by the doping, a photo-generated hole is quickly filled by one of the very numerous electrons. Likewise, in the region doped so that there is an abundance of freed holes, any photo-generated electron quickly drops into one of the ubiquitous holes. So the material far from the junction is no use to us.

The interesting case is where the photo-generated electron and hole are created in the exclusion zone, since the strong electrical force here will sweep the electron up to the safety of the upper half (n-type) where freed electrons thrive. Meanwhile, the hole is swept down into the security of a haven for freed holes (the p-type material). The exclusion zone pumps apart any separated charge appearing within it. This is the photovoltaic action we were looking for.

▼Other p–n junctions▲ can be used for functions other than electricity generation.

▼Other p–n junctions▲

The electronics industry uses p–n junctions in the same way that the construction industry uses bricks: they are a basic building block. We discussed light-emitting diodes (LEDs) in Block 4 Part 3. You may know that the laser in a compact disc player uses a laser diode working in tandem with a photodiode detector. Both are based on p–n junctions. Transistors and integrated circuits comprise combinations of p–n junctions.

The word *diode* is often linked to p–n junctions. Diode simply means 'two electrode'; implying two electrical connections. Back in the early days of electronics, valves came with two, three, five or more electrodes, so a diode was the simplest valve. Moreover, diode valves only conducted current in one direction – you couldn't put them in 'backwards'. That characteristic link to current flow in one direction only transferred into semiconductor electronics when it was noted that p–n junctions mimic valve diodes: they tend to conduct electrons easily in one direction (from p to n) and hardly at all in the other (from n to p); see Figure 2.18.

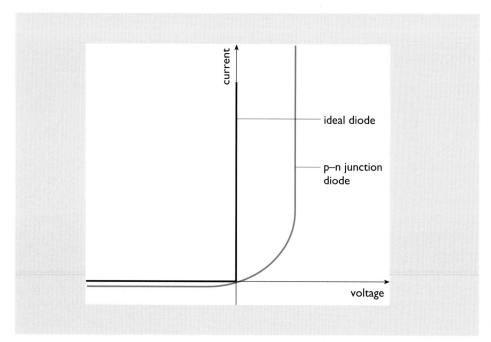

Figure 2.18 The characteristic *V–I* curve of a p–n diode

A photovoltaic solar cell is made from a slice of semiconductor doped to give the two-layer structure we have just considered. Electrical connections are made to top and bottom to collect the electrons and holes generated by light penetrating to the junction region. The top contact has not only to collect current but also to allow light to pass, so it either has to be transparent or it must be a pattern of fine fingers that do not obscure too much of the top surface; see Figure 2.19.

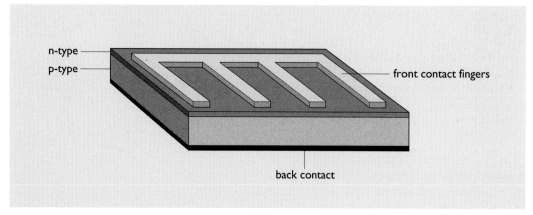

Figure 2.19 A schematic of a solar cell

Identify the two key functions of semiconductor material within a photovoltaic cell.

3.3 Photovoltaic performance

The finished cell, when illuminated by light, behaves very much like a conventional electrochemical cell. In fact, a bank of solar cells is sometimes called a 'solar battery'. With a positive contact on the surface of the p-type, and a negative contact on the surface of the n-type, the cell can be used as a source of d.c. (direct current) energy in an electric circuit.

It is good engineering practice to have an idea of what limitations there may be to the performance of a device. I will show you here some of the limits for a photocell; it helps to identify where the scope lies for optimization.

3.3.1 Upper limit to the current

In Section 3.2 I asked you to make an estimate of the number of photons per square metre per second associated with the standard test condition of 1000 W m^{-2} at AM1.5. Let's use this figure to investigate how much current a photocell could generate.

I described in Block 4 Part 3 how electric current is associated with the movement of electrons. The unit of current, the amp, corresponds to a flow of electric charge equal to one coulomb per second, where the coulomb is a unit of charge, given the symbol C. The charge on an electron is 1.6×10^{-19} C, so it takes a lot of electrons to generate a single amp!

If each photon releases an electron, with the exclusion zone pushing it into the external circuit, the current in amps per square metre would be:

1.6×10^{-19} (the charge on each electron) in coulombs $\times 3 \times 10^{21}$ (the photon flux) in photons per second per square metre = 480 amps per square metre

However, not all of the photons in sunlight will be above the threshold energy for the semiconducting material, depending on which material is used. For silicon, about 10% of the photons in sunlight are below the threshold energy and cannot release charge to supply the current. Furthermore, only a fraction of the photons will penetrate the material to reach the exclusion zone, depending on what steps are taken to prevent wasteful reflections and absorptions outside the exclusion zone. So don't expect high efficiencies!

3.3.2 Upper limit to the e.m.f.

The e.m.f. generated by a solar cell is zero in the absence of any illumination and initially rises rapidly when illumination begins, changing more slowly as the light level rises further. The maximum e.m.f. the cell can achieve is governed by the threshold energy of the material from which it is made. It's not obvious, but it transpires that the energy (or 'push') given to each electron pushed out by a photocell can't exceed the threshold energy of the material used to make the p–n junction. This means, effectively, that the maximum e.m.f. a cell can achieve, expressed of course in volts, is simply related to the threshold energy, expressed in electron volts. With silicon the threshold energy is 1.1 eV, and so the maximum possible silicon cell voltage is 1.1 V.

Note that the e.m.f. limit is set by the threshold energy of the material involved in the energy conversion and not by the energy of the photon. So a 2.2 eV photon, captured by silicon (threshold energy 1.1 eV) is already half wasted, electrically speaking. Once again, don't expect high efficiencies!

3.3.3 Actual current and actual e.m.f.

So, currents are inevitably less than we estimated above, because not every photon that reaches the cell launches an electron into the external circuit. Some simply don't have enough energy to liberate an electron; some are reflected; others are blocked by the top electrode; some are absorbed outside the exclusion zone; for some of the photons which actually get to the right place the electron–hole pairs they create recombine before use can be made of them. A more conservative estimate of the maximum available current is 240 A m^{-2} (half of what we estimated in Section 3.3.1) (you should be able to show that this is the same as 24 mA cm^{-2}).

And in practice, the cell e.m.f. at the operating light level gets only about halfway towards the limit set by the threshold energy. A very high intensity of illumination is needed for the full 1.1 V to be generated, so a silicon photocell at 0.6 V is doing pretty well. There's scope here for good design to shave away some of the losses in current and e.m.f. performance.

3.3.4 Power output

Let's see how much power a silicon photocell might be expected to produce. Electrical power is the product of current and voltage (in this case the e.m.f. of the cell).

The amount of power a cell generates depends on three things: the material of the cell, its area and the amount of sunlight falling upon it. We have just established that for a typical silicon cell in full sunlight (AM1.5, 1000 W m^{-2}) the current per unit area of cell is about 24 mA cm^{-2}. This is delivered at the cell e.m.f., so the power per unit area for a silicon cell is as follows.

P = current per unit area × e.m.f.

   = 24 mA cm^{-2} × 0.6 V

   = 14.4 mW cm^{-2}

   = 144 W m^{-2} (There are 10 000 cm^2 in 1 m^2)

As the total incident power density is 1000 W m^{-2}, this is equivalent to a conversion efficiency of about 14%; we weren't expecting high efficiency.

Exercise 2.8

According to our estimates the power output of silicon photocells can be expected to be no more than about 14 mW cm^{-2} for the AM1.5, 1000 W m^{-2} standard. Estimate the area of silicon photocell that would be required for a satellite requiring 1 kW and operating in Low Earth Orbit (AM0).

Semiconductors are not such good conductors as metals. Photocurrent generated inside a semiconductor has inevitably to pass through some of this 'not so good' conductor. Ohm's law tells us to expect a voltage drop when currents encounter resistance. The I–V characteristic of a photocell maps the real performance in terms of current (I) and e.m.f. (V). See Figure 2.20.

Just as with a battery, the current that a photovoltaic cell will supply depends on the resistance of the load put across it. Without any load connected, i.e. an 'open circuit', the e.m.f. is termed the open circuit voltage (V_{OC}); we estimated this to be about 0.6 V for silicon. Because there is no load connected, the current is zero and so the power, the rate at which the cell transfers energy or does work ($P = VI$), equals zero.

If on the other hand the cell is short-circuited (i.e. one terminal connected directly to the other) with virtually zero resistance between the terminals,

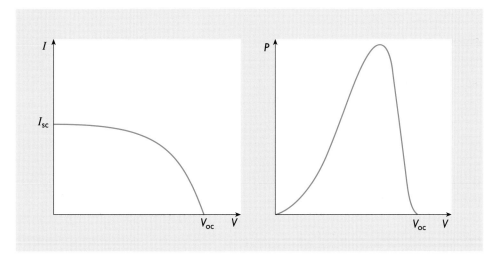

Figure 2.20 (a) The *I*–*V* characteristic of a photocell (b) The power output from a photocell

then the maximum current flows. This is the short circuit current (I_{SC}). As the resistance is zero, the e.m.f. output is forced to be zero (Ohm's law, $V = IR$) and so the power is again zero.

Between these two extremes the current varies from 0 to I_{SC} and the e.m.f. from V_{OC} to 0, as shown in Figure 2.20(a). There is an optimum condition at which the power delivered, the product of the current and the e.m.f., is at a maximum; see Figure 2.20(b). Thus, PV system designers need to be advised of the optimum power at which photocells should be operated whenever possible.

The output of photocells falls to zero when the light goes out. ▼Working in the dark▲ is something that it would be wise to accommodate.

3.4 Selecting a material for PV cells

The most important material property for PV cells is the threshold energy. Table 2.2 shows values for a range of simple and compound semiconductors. Based on our previous discussion you should be able to say something about what to look for in a semiconductor that is to be used in a PV system.

Table 2.2 Threshold energy in a range of semiconducting materials

Threshold energy/eV	Semiconducting material	
0.17	InSb	Indium antimonide
0.31	PbTe	Lead telluride
0.36	InAs	Indium arsenide
0.41	PbS	Lead sulphide
0.61	Ge	Germanium
0.72	GaSb	Gallium antimonide
1.12	Si	Silicon
1.35	InP	Indium phosphide
1.42	GaAs	Gallium arsenide
1.56	CdTe	Cadmium telluride
1.70	CdSe	Cadmium sulphide
2.26	GaP	Gallium phosphide
2.42	CdS	Cadmium sulphide
3.00	SiC	Silicon carbide
3.36	GaN	Gallium nitride
3.68	ZnS	Zinc sulphide

▼Working in the dark▲

Although solar cells behave to some extent like batteries, they are actually very different devices. A battery is a means of chemically storing energy, whereas a solar cell is a source of electricity whilst the Sun shines.

A hybrid system combines these two aspects, with a solar cell charging a rechargeable battery. The battery provides electricity for the load, whatever it is, at night (i.e. when there is no sunlight). During the day, the solar cell provides electricity for supplying the load and also for recharging the battery. Clearly the design of the solar cell needs to allow extra area over and above that required to capture enough energy for the load, so that there is sufficient extra capacity to refill the chemical store.

Exercise 2.9

Identify the problem, in terms of available output power, with choosing too high a value for the threshold energy.

Exercise 2.10

Identify the problem with choosing too low a value for the threshold voltage.

The optimum threshold energy is at about 1.5 eV, so materials such as gallium arsenide (GaAs) and cadmium telluride (CdTe) look promising. But working with silicon is second nature to the electronics industry, considerably easier than working with the more exotic and expensive semiconductors such as GaAs and CdTe. In the electronics industry methods for purifying silicon, growing big crystals, doping, cutting and connecting it, are well known. It's no surprise that silicon, though far from ideal as a PV material, remains a popular choice for solar cells. The materials listed in Table 2.2, including silicon, are used as pure, single crystals. Amorphous silicon, which is discussed in Section 4, is an altogether different type of material, and it is particularly amenable to mass manufacture of PV cells, introducing useful competition to the market.

The reason for the optimum value of 1.5 eV for the threshold energy is because of the shape of the standard spectrum in Figure 2.8(b). The threshold energy needs to be low enough so that a reasonably large number of photons are collected. Notice that 1.5 eV is below the peak value of the spectrum, just on the border between visible and infrared. The threshold energy also needs to be high enough that a reasonable voltage is generated. This leads to the threshold voltage compromise.

The optimum varies slightly with the particular spectrum. The spectrum in space has higher blue content and so for this environment cells could usefully be made from a material with a larger threshold energy.

3.5 Summary

Sunlight (indeed all electromagnetic radiation) comes in discrete packets of energy called photons. Photons in the visible light range have energies of 2–3 eV.

The sunlight received on Earth consists of photons with a range of energies centred on visible light, peaking around 3 eV. These photons have penetrated through the atmosphere. Many other photons never reach the surface of the Earth, being either scattered or absorbed by the atmosphere. This results in a spectrum of light that varies with latitude, time of day and weather. Various international standards have been agreed upon for the purpose of meaningful comparisons of performance – the main one being an Air Mass 1.5 (AM1.5) spectrum at a total power of 1 kW m^{-2}.

Photons can be absorbed by semiconductors – *if the photon energy is greater than the semiconductor's threshold energy*. Visible light is absorbed by semiconductor materials such as silicon and cadmium sulphide. Absorption generates electron–hole pairs. Semiconductor conductivity can be influenced by absorption of photons and by doping: p-type material is doped to have a population of freed holes; n-type material is doped to have a population of freed electrons. To make photovoltaic devices, electrons and holes are prevented from immediately recombining by using the electric forces within a p–n junction to separate them. The photovoltaic (PV) solar cell combines a shallow p–n junction with a transparent contact to the front and a non-transparent contact to the back.

A silicon PV cell can be expected to generate about 14 mW cm^{-2} at an e.m.f. of 0.6 V, and AM1.5 conditions.

The performance of a PV cell can be assessed by measuring its *I–V* characteristic. High resistance and short circuits must be avoided to optimize the efficiency of conversion of sunlight to electricity.

The best materials for PV cells have a threshold energy of about 1.5 eV. Silicon has a threshold energy of 1.1 eV, which is a bit low, but because of its extensive use in electronics and the high purity that can be obtained, it is widely used for PV cells. Compound semiconductors such as gallium arsenide have a threshold energy close to the ideal of 1.5 eV but are much more expensive.

There are two generic approaches to the manufacture of photovoltaic cells: either one must aim for high efficiency to give more power for a given area; or one seeks cheaper processing to give lower costs per watt of installed capacity. The former favours single crystal (or monocrystalline) materials; the latter is a job for amorphous material. See ▼**One crystal, many crystals and no crystals at all**▲.

4.1 Bulk processing of single crystal cells

Silicon is the most widely used material for PV cells. Single crystal cells are manufactured using the standard techniques developed by the semiconductor industry over the last forty years.

Silicon occurs naturally all over the place, in combination with oxygen in sand and in quartz as silicon dioxide, and in other minerals as silicates. It is extracted from silicon dioxide in much the same way that iron is extracted from its oxide: heating with coke (see Block 3 Part 2). The resulting silicon is nowhere near pure enough for semiconductor work, so it is cleaned up by combining it with chlorine to form silicon tetrachloride, a liquid which is then readily purified by repeated distillation. Converting this back to silicon involves more heating, this time with hydrogen. Before making the grade for electronics use, it is purified even more by elaborate processes, after which you can call it 'pure' silicon because there will be fewer than one atom in every billion that is not silicon.

The next stage is to grow single crystals of silicon from molten pure silicon. Silicon melts at 1500 °C, and so this is an energy-intensive process.

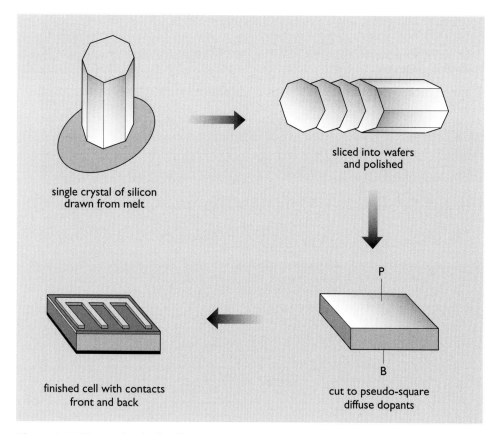

single crystal of silicon
drawn from melt

sliced into wafers
and polished

P

B

cut to pseudo-square
diffuse dopants

finished cell with contacts
front and back

Figure 2.21 Processing bulk silicon

▼One crystal, many crystals and no crystals at all▲

Lumps of most solid materials are an agglomeration of lots of crystals (often called 'grains') that have grown into each other. All metals, all ceramics and many plastics are 'naturally' like this.

Making large single crystals is an expensive business. Sometimes the benefits are worth the effort. For instance, some turbine blades in aero-engines owe their strength to the fact that each one is solidified as a giant single crystal, achieving an astonishing degree of perfection at the atomic scale.

Another example comes from electronics. The microelectronics industry could never have come of age without the mass production of complex components of astounding reliability. The use of wafers cut from a single crystal of silicon was essential to the production of sufficiently pure, uniform, near-perfect, material with which to build circuits.

For microelectronics, the role of the single crystal structure of the wafer is to provide an ultra-clean atomic platform with a pattern of hills and valleys exactly right for growing new silicon. The microcircuits are built in the newly grown layer; most of the original silicon is 'dead weight' in electronics terms, but provides mechanical integrity.

The cost of a mass produced item is always under scrutiny. The use of material that is not single crystal offers considerable cost reduction, provided performance can be maintained. Even more attractive is the thought that silicon deposits of the required size for any given microcircuit can be placed upon a variety of surfaces, without the need for growing large crystals and cutting them up. Sure enough, electronics-grade silicon is now available in a completely non-crystalline form, amorphous silicon. It can also be made pure enough as an agglomeration of lots of crystals – called 'polysilicon' in the electronics world and 'multi-crystalline' silicon in the photovoltaics world.

The crystal is grown using a small seed crystal that establishes the orientation of the atomic crystal lattice for the large crystal. The crystal is rotated as it is pulled from the melt, and the molten silicon solidifies on its surface in a near-perfect arrangement of atoms. Single crystals of 30 cm diameter and 1.5 m long can be grown in this way. It's not something you do as a hobby though; this is a specialist business.

The structure of 'electronics-grade silicon', as it is called, is close to perfect, with fewer than one atom per billion being an impurity or out of place. In fact, it is so pure that only careful electronic measurements can detect any imperfection – one such test could be based on the efficiency of a photovoltaic p–n junction.

The next stage is to cut the crystal into wafers about 0.5 mm thick, and then to polish them. This is precision work, done by specialists; if you want to make PVs you'll probably buy in ready cut and polished wafers, already doped either n-type or p-type, rather than make them yourself.

To fabricate a photocell a p–n junction must then be formed just below one surface. To do this, dopant atoms of the opposite type to those already doping the wafer are diffused into the wafers from one side only. That is, if you have a wafer doped uniformly with phosphorus (n-type dopant) then boron atoms (p-type dopant) diffused in at a higher concentration can convert a section of the material to p-type silicon. Diffusion of dopant is a slow process even at 1000 °C, and diffusion of atoms to a point a few micrometres beneath the surface, and hence the formation of the p–n junction, usually takes several hours.

To complete the PV cell, contacts are put on front and back, usually metals deposited by evaporation. The back contact can cover the whole surface, but the front contact has to allow light to reach the cell and so is arranged in fingers that obscure less than 3% of the front surface area.

Multi-crystalline silicon (mc-Si)

An alternative low budget 'recipe' uses wafers of multi-crystalline silicon. Subsequent sawing, diffusion and contacting are the same as used for monocrystalline silicon. Of course, with cheap, structurally imperfect material the efficiency of PVs made this way may be rather lower, but in cases where light and space are plentiful, or power needs are modest, this may be acceptable.

4.2 Thin film processing

A different approach for the processing of such cells uses processes capable of much higher throughput, again at the expense of material quality and efficiency of PV cells.

Thin films of semiconductor are deposited on a substrate, often glass (transparent) or materials such as stainless steel. The processes used all take place at much lower temperatures (220–300 °C) than crystalline manufacture, and so are less energy intensive, and are thereby inherently cheaper.

There is a very wide range of these processes, but they are all fairly amenable to continuous (or semi-continuous) production, through conveyor techniques. Hence, they are capable of large cost reductions per unit through economies of scale.

One of the contacts has to be transparent, to allow light to reach the junction. So when building this contact, a transparent conductor must be deposited onto the substrate before the semiconductor film is deposited. Certain oxide semiconductors have the required properties. The other contact, however, does not have to be transparent.

The semiconductors are deposited in at least two layers to make up the p–n junction (i.e. the p–n junction is not created by diffusion processes as in crystalline silicon, but by layering of differently doped semiconductors). The final contact is deposited on the top-most semiconductor. This can be opaque if a transparent glass substrate has been used, but must be transparent for a stainless steel substrate. A popular choice for a transparent conductor is a tin oxide doped (more controlled impurity) with indium.

An advantage of thin films is that they make better use of expensive semiconductor material, using it only where it is required for photovoltaic purposes. (The bulk processing methods 'waste' purified material in using it for mechanical support of the active PV layer.)

There is a variety of ways to produce and modify thin films. Evaporation involves heating a solid source in a vacuum until it vaporizes and deposits on the substrate. Related methods use low pressure gases, broken down by the application of a high voltage, to 'engineer' the surface appropriately. In electrodeposition, a substrate is placed in an aqueous solution of the desired semiconductors. A charge applied to the substrate attracts the ions in the solution to deposit on its surface.

The films deposited by all these processes are very rough in comparison to crystalline silicon and the material quality is inferior. This leads to lower and more variable efficiency, often as low as 5% in production.

See ▼Materials for thin film cells▲ for more details of the semiconductors that can be used.

SAQ 2.8 (Learning outcome 2.8)

Briefly summarize the advantages and disadvantages of bulk processing and thin film production of PV cells.

At the start of this section, mention was made of a dichotomy in development between bulk and thin film techniques aiming for the different goals of high efficiency or low cost, respectively. However, several processes are being

▼Materials for thin film cells▲

Amorphous silicon can be deposited as a vapour in several layers. Because it has no long-range structure (i.e. there is no local ordering of the atoms) it has a lot of defects and this leads to low efficiencies of about 5%. These can be offset by incorporation of extra layers in the cell that contain not only amorphous silicon but also amorphous germanium (Ge). These extra layers absorb additional parts of the solar spectrum with longer wavelength, and so boost the performance of the cells by up to 13% in the laboratory (under 'perfect' conditions) or by about 8% in production (where compromises in quality have to be made to offset the costs).

Other materials used for thin films again involve compounds. Cadmium telluride (CdTe) is the most appropriate of these, having a threshold energy of 1.5 eV. It is deposited as a polycrystalline material by electrodeposition or evaporation and cells can be made with efficiencies of up to 16% in the laboratory or 10% in production.

Cadmium, however, is a highly toxic material. Although this can be contained in production, use and decommissioning, it is still desirable to find alternatives.

Unfortunately the options are limited for simple binary compounds, so it is necessary to move to three-element (ternary) compounds. The most widely used of these at present is copper indium diselenide ($CuInSe_2$ or CIS). The most efficient thin film cells so far have been made from CIS (about 17%). Unfortunately, selenium is also toxic, ten times less so than cadmium, but still to be avoided if possible. Another ternary compound is copper indium disulphide ($CuInS_2$). It is now being researched as a very promising material, but a means of producing $CuInS_2$ cells as efficient as those made of CIS is yet to be found.

Ternary compounds and four-element (called 'quaternary') compounds offer a very large range of possibilities for engineering PV materials. However, it is hard to believe that such exotic materials are necessary in pursuit of higher efficiency and improved productivity, though there has been a logical progression towards these goals.

developed that occupy the middle ground between these two. There are processes which are seeking to reduce the cost of crystalline silicon, by re-using expensive substrates and having several layers of lower quality cheaper material. Others are seeking to increase the efficiency of thin film materials and the structures into which they are formed.

4.3 Summary

There are two main routes for PV processing: bulk and thin film. The former produces higher quality, more efficient cells, but is more expensive. The latter offers lower processing costs but at the expense of material quality and efficiency.

Efficiency depends both on the suitability of the particular material (mainly its threshold energy) and the processing method. The thin film processes are inherently cheaper for a given area but the bulk processes produce better material. The two routes lead to cells with about the same cost per peak watt of output.

5 PV systems

It is all very well to have invented a novel power source, but to be useful it has to be integrated into a system that uses it to advantage over other sources. A complete PV system consists of two subsystems. First there is the power source itself, an array of cells. The second subsystem forms a so-called 'power-conditioning interface' between the array and the load.

The easiest way to build arrays of anything is from smaller, standardized modules – it's the same approach that builders have used for generations, using arrays of ready-made bricks and tiles of arbitrary size and shape for constructing walls and roofs. Modules of PV cells are therefore constructed in standard-sized packages. In the following discussion, crystalline silicon cells are used as the exemplar. Most of the aspects of the systems apply equally to the other types of cell.

5.1 Modules and arrays

Modules are collections of cells connected in series and/or parallel to give a reasonable combination of voltage and current. It is not surprising that a popular choice for the voltage of a module is between 15 and 18 V – enough to charge a 12 V battery.

The size of modules is chosen so that one person can easily lift and handle them, for ease of installation – about 1 m × 0.5 m. However, the larger a module is, the more efficient it is, because there is less 'dead' space around the edge for a given area. I've never noticed ease of installation being much of an issue in determining the size of windows, though I now suppose that it may be. What do you think?

Modules are finished with an aluminium frame to protect the edges or left as laminates for integration into architectural facades. An integral terminal box ensures ease of connection.

Exercise 2.11

(a) Look back to Section 3.3 and complete the following for a silicon solar cell measuring 10 cm × 10 cm, at standard AM1.5 conditions.

Typical output voltage ……….

Current available from 10 cm × 10 cm = ……….

(b) Suggest how to connect cells specified in (a) to furnish a module that will drive 2.4 A at 18 V.

(c) Suggest how to arrange the cells in (a) and estimate the dimensions of the module.

Encapsulation

The cells and the connectors between them are sandwiched between a layer of glass on the front and a polymer film on the back. They are sealed under pressure to ensure protection from the elements. Encapsulation is critical to the life of the module. If water gets inside it will corrode the contacts and the module will fail. It is very seldom that the cells themselves fail. With proper encapsulation the modules should have an active life in excess of 30 years.

A photovoltaic array is an arrangement of modules. The number and positioning depend on the area available (such as a roof) and the nature of the load to be supplied.

Thin film modules

Large-area cells can be constructed from thin film materials, making modules simpler. A large, single-cell module on a flexible substrate sounds like something that could have advantages in a competitive market. In practice, thin film cells are not as stable as those based on crystalline materials and are predicted to have lives of about 20 years.

5.2 Power conditioning

Solar energy is a variable resource; it is likely that the supply will not often match the demand on a minute-by-minute basis. Come to think of it, it is possible that on a sunny day my energy requirements might be less than usual, as I won't require heating or lighting – though this may be countered by the need for air conditioning perhaps? And another important energy use is agricultural irrigation in summer months when the sunlight resource is greatest. However, for most other applications some form of energy storage is required. In the short term, variations in brightness occur as cloud cover changes; longer term variations of course are imposed by the passage of the Sun across the sky. Equipment to match the output of a PV array to an energy storage scheme is an important component of a PV system.

5.2.1 Batteries

Battery storage is very widely used in the type of stand-alone application that it is not convenient to connect to the grid, whether using PV modules, diesel generators or wind turbines. Batteries are just as modular as PV, so the combined system can easily be scaled as demand or finances dictate. Batteries have similar electrical performance to PV, both being d.c. devices with similar characteristics. Many loads designed to run on batteries are suitable for running directly from PV.

Lead–acid batteries are bulky and heavy. They suffer if they undergo repeated deep discharge, so a large over-capacity is required to ensure that in normal operation only about the top 20% of the battery's capacity is used. The motor industry has ensured the availability of lead–acid batteries that seemingly thrive on daily fast drain-and-trickle-charge cycles for years at a stretch. For working alongside PV systems, though, a different design of the battery plates is better for the 'long drain–long charge' cycle.

Batteries are good for short-period storage of relatively small amounts of energy, and are ideal for the day–night cycle and periods of bad weather, but are less suitable for the summer–winter cycle of solar availability.

5.2.2 d.c. to a.c. conversion

In order to feed a power source such as a PV system into the mains supply, the e.m.f. has to be matched. To do this the output from the PV system has to be converted from d.c. to a.c. This is a standard task, and is done using an electronic device called an inverter. The inverter detects the instantaneous e.m.f. of the mains and turns the d.c. input up and down in synchronism. It then feeds the modulated d.c. to a transformer that steps the voltage up appropriately. Stringent conditions have to be met in order that the waveform of the generated e.m.f. matches the mains, introducing no spikes in voltage that could be damaging. Modern inverters meet these criteria and achieve an efficiency of around 90%. They often incorporate an automatic isolator to switch off the supply if there is no mains detected. If the mains is turned off for maintenance, then there must be no possibility of electric shock from the PV array powering the local system. I think I'd like a big switch that I can see as well, so I could be sure it was switched off before I started work!

The disadvantage of the automatic-isolation safety feature is that such a PV system cannot be used as a back-up in the event of a power outage – this is often an important reason for wanting a PV system in the first place. There are also inverters that do not have this cut-out protection that can be connected to PV panels independent of the mains, so that 230 V a.c. devices can be operated in a stand-alone system.

SAQ 2.9 (Learning outcome 2.9)

Consider a battery-powered system that uses PV recharging. It has a lead–acid battery, specifically designed for remote application and for deep discharge. The battery has a 24 A h capacity at 18 V. Assume the construction of modules is as described in Section 5.1 (e.m.f. = 18 V and current = 2.4 A).

Estimate how many modules would be required to charge this battery from complete discharge, at a location receiving an average daily equivalent[1] of 2 hours of sunshine at 1000 W m^{-2}.

5.3 Large scale power generation

PV arrays can be and are used in very large systems providing power to the mains network. These can be in remote locations. They sometimes have modules that track the Sun across the sky. This means that the angle of the Sun to the module is ideal for a much larger proportion of the day. They can also incorporate reflective surfaces on the side of the modules to reflect light towards the cells. But these systems increase complexity by introducing moving parts. In general such systems are not suitable for the UK climate, not so much because of the lower level of overall sunshine, but because a fair proportion of daylight is diffuse and so not suitable for tracking.

Although not viable in direct competition with fossil fuel and nuclear power stations, PV power stations are competitive for peak power generation, particularly for applications such as air conditioning.

In the current UK deregulated electricity environment (2001), the power companies bid for half-hour slots of generation. At times of peak use the value of these bids can go very high. Small generating companies based on large PV installations and those based on other renewables only have to bid when they want. Hence they can choose to export to the grid at those times when they can get good prices.

Hybrid systems for stand-alone applications

PV modules can be used in parallel with another power source, such as a wind turbine, a small hydro-turbine or a diesel generator together with a battery store. This evens out the seasonal availability of solar energy, and is particularly complementary with wind power, as in temperate climates like that of the UK, wind is more abundant in the winter and sunlight is more so in the summer. For the same reason this reduces the amount of over-capacity required in a battery bank, as the periods when there is likely to be no charging of the batteries is shorter. The disadvantages are that these are more complex systems, and it is difficult to design a system that works well under all conditions because of the different characteristics of the power generation. Furthermore, the range of suitable sites for locating such systems is more restricted and likely to be a compromise between resources.

---

[1] In fact, the day's dose of energy would actually arrive at a lower power and over a longer time period.

5.4 PVs for the home and office

Buffering a PV system by interfacing it to the mains means that during the summer and times of abundant sunlight the consumer uses PV electricity and manages to export some to the mains. In the winter or at night, energy is drawn back from the mains. Let's see if a small domestic installation is viable.

Exercise 2.12

My electricity usage in the last twelve months was for lighting, supplementary heating and the normal domestic chores, but not for main space-heating, nor for cooking. It amounted to 3347 kW h. The point to address is this: can I capture this much solar energy on my roof, storing it somehow? Complete the following statements.

(a) The total energy electrical energy I use is apparently
.................W h year^{-1} or, averaged over 365 days, ...W h day^{-1}.
(I could do the sum in *joules* per year or per day (multiplying by 3600), but I think it's simpler to complete the sums in *watt hours* per year or per day.)

(b) The AM1.5 calculations that we have done before gave a typical silicon PV output of 14 mW cm^{-2}. Taking account of the latitude of Milton Keynes (means less power per unit area) I'm going to reduce the figure and say that I can expect only 8 mW cm^{-2}. I'm also going to suggest that in this area there is an average of four hours of sunlight close to midday (a rather ambitious assumption) during which I can expect the AM1.5 conditions to apply. I can therefore hope to capture an energy per unit area of ....W h cm^{-2} day^{-1} and after 365 days
..............W h cm^{-2} year^{-1}.

(c) To gather all the electrical energy I need in one year I need to deploy enough area. Let's say I need E W h year^{-1} (that's the figure calculated in (a)); the rate at which I can gather energy I'll call Y W h cm^{-2} year^{-1} (that's the figure calculated in (b)); the collection area is A cm^2. So

E (W h year^{-1}) = Y (W h cm^{-2} year^{-1}) $\times A$ (cm^2)

or $A = E/Y$ cm^2

So is that a reasonable area? Work it out; it comes out in square centimetres if you use my figures so divide by 10^4 to get a result in square metres.

Area = ...m^2

Comment: Well my roof area is only a little less than that so I'm in with a chance, provided there is a way to match the supply to the demand.

The exercise shows that small domestic installations may be *energetically* viable in central England. It would take a south-facing unshaded roof area of about 30 m^2. This applies to many suburban roofs. There are three important points to note. First, this system proposed is not independent of the mains, so standing charges for mains connection are still levied. Second, only about 30% of non-seasonal domestic energy use is electrical; the other 70% is used for heating and cooking, which is partly seasonal (you want more heating when there is less sunlight). Finally, to be *economically* viable, the cost of installation needs to be recovered from the saving on the charges for each kW h of electricity that does not have to be bought. I wonder how many years that will take? Of course, the simple estimates made above need to be validated by field trials; see Figure 2.22 for an example test site where several PV modules are on trial.

PV installation on office buildings is a large growth area in the UK, because of the beneficial aspects of a 'green' corporate image. Furthermore, many office

Figure 2.22 The Environmental Change Institute (Oxford University) PV test site at Begbroke, Oxon

Figure 2.23 A solar powered calculator

cladding materials are very expensive, so the use of architecturally integrated PV modules can be not much of a price increase over conventional cladding, whilst providing some power for the building and a favourable image for the enterprise.

Consumer products

Watches and calculators (Figure 2.23) have long used small amorphous silicon cells as power sources. These use early-generation amorphous silicon that is less efficient than modern material, but because the power requirements are so low with liquid crystal displays, and because the alternative batteries are relatively expensive, such cells are viable. More recently, a number of other products have become available, such as garden lights with built-in batteries, pond fountains, solar battery chargers for NiCd batteries, etc. These usually use amorphous silicon cells and in general have the cells designed to be an integral part of the device. As such they are unobtrusive and hence more acceptable.

5.5 Summary

Photovoltaic systems include a lot more technology than the PV cells alone. The systems are fabricated from modules of cells, in a structure for mounting the modules, with a means of power conditioning to match the requirements of the load to be supplied. D.c. storage in batteries extends availability through the night and in bad weather. Conversion to a.c. using inverters enables mains-like supplies in remote applications or export to the real mains.

It is possible to use PV for large scale power generation through very large PV installations, although it is preferable to use the embedded generation of roof and office-based systems to support the conventional mains supply and to make a substantial contribution to overall electricity generation.

6 Economics, environmental impact and integration

The costs of using PV technology go beyond those of the manufacture of modular arrays of solar cells; there are many other costs in PV systems. A simple formula relating investment to return would require a detailed knowledge of any subsidies and charges associated with PV electricity. It's a task for the accountants.

All manufacturing processes have some environmental impact. As the main reason for the implementation of PV is to reduce the environmental impact of energy generation, it is crucial that the benefits outweigh the impact of manufacture.

In the large scale implementation of PV and other renewable energy systems, other factors, such as the impact on the infrastructure of the national supply grid, have to be considered. A grid that relies heavily on erratic, renewable sources will need special measures to keep it stable.

6.1 Economics and implementation

The quantity 'euros per watt in peak sunshine (€ W_p^{-1})' is a measure of the price of a module in euros divided by the number of watts it will produce in peak sunshine. It is useful for comparing the price of different module types and shows long term trends. The € W_p^{-1} prices of PV modules have fallen dramatically as the market has increased over the last two decades or so, as shown in Figure 2.24.

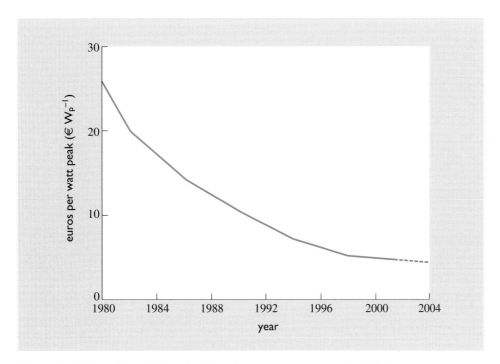

Figure 2.24 The price of PV technology in euros per watt peak, € W_p^{-1}

The price of a PV module is only part of the cost of a complete system. Total costs break down into three main areas: the cost of the PV modules; the cost of the support structure; and the cost of installation. In northern Europe, systems are most commonly installed on building roofs or south-facing walls, so I'm not going to consider cost and availability of land in the economic argument.

Support structure costs are a particular problem for retro-fitted units, where the system cost is, say, added to that of the roof. For new buildings and renovation, the cost of architecturally-integrated PV-cladding and PV-roofing units can be integrated into the cost of the standard cladding or roofing.

Installation costs are high for two reasons. First, installation is a specialist electrical task, involving a d.c. power system. Second, the installations are individually tailored to each site.

Schemes are available for PV mortgages on better terms than standard unsecured loans. These spread the capital costs over several years, and although this does not as yet make them truly viable, it can make them affordable.

With grid-connected systems the price one gets for exporting PV-generated electricity to the utility is often less than that paid for importing it from the utility, making actual monetary payback time much longer than the energy payback time. However, at the time of writing, some utilities offer 'net-metering', which means getting the same price for exported electricity as that paid for imported electricity – effectively running the meter backwards. There are calls for improving this still further, as in Germany, with a tariff that gives a substantially *higher* price for the exported power. One argument in favour of this approach is that to make 1 kW h of electrical energy from a thermal source such as a fossil fuel power station takes 3 kW h of *thermal* energy. This means that a PV kilowatt-hour is 'worth' three thermal kilowatt-hours. Other arguments are that embedded generation is useful to a utility, in order to maintain supply at weak points in the system. Added value can also accrue from avoiding the losses involved in power transmission.

Germany has good subsidy rates, and other countries, such as Australia, are following suit. But ironically these can sometimes be *too* high. Subsidies of 90% in India resulted in a large number of installations, but when these were audited it was found that three times as many systems had been sold as were actually in place! The reason was that systems were being resold over the border in Nepal.

6.2 Large scale implementation

Module fabrication is essentially the same for all cell types, and is a very different sort of process from cell manufacture. It therefore lends itself to the establishment of independent module fabrication facilities that are able to handle a number of different initial cell materials. This enables local fabrication using local labour, which is not dependent on high technology nor particularly sensitive to the cell materials. The same PV modules may be built from different components. The performance of the final assembly in different complete installations is a crucial engineering test.

As the number of installations increases, the prices of systems come down and domestic-embedded generation becomes more and more viable. When the amount of electricity generated by PV installations reaches about 10% of the total amount of electrical energy available from the national grid, the grid will no longer act as an effective store. This is because the seasonal nature of the energy supply will be too erratic for the grid demand. Electricity generation by all renewables in the UK in 2000 was about 1%, with PV contributing a small, but growing fraction.

Exercise 2.13

A medium to long term problem for PV, and for renewables in general, is the question of energy storage. What's needed is the energy equivalent of a portfolio of investment accounts covering short, medium and long terms.

Suggest two ways that energy from PV can be stored. Think in broad terms about the answer, and consider all the different forms of 'energy' and energy storage that you've encountered in the course. Comment in each case on the storage timescale, and any environmental issues.

6.3 Environmental impact

There are two factors to consider here. First is the effect on the environment of any materials used in the manufacture of cells, modules, arrays, systems and finished installations. Second is the effect of embodied energy – that energy invested in the manufacture and disposal of exhausted or out-of-date installations. The assessment of these factors is brought together in a *life-cycle analysis* in terms of the inventory from 'cradle to grave' of pollutants released and of the total energy used. These figures can be compared with the relevant figures for conventional electricity generation of the same capacity.

PV modules have a pretty clean sheet during their operational life. They emit no pollutants. Fossil fuel energy used in production, installation and decommissioning, however, gives rise to both embodied energy and net emission of pollutants such as carbon dioxide (CO_2), sulphur dioxide (SO_2) and the oxides of nitrogen (N_2O, NO and NO_2, collectively called 'nox', NO_x) and particulates.

6.3.1 Materials and pollution

There are various chemicals and solvents used in both bulk and thin film processing. No heavy metals, with their associated toxicity problems, are used in silicon cell production, either in bulk processing or in amorphous thin film. Cyanide compounds and toxic gases are used, however, but these are controlled by burn-off, good practice and recycling; in this regard the industry is no worse than many other 'high-tech' processes.

Some of the exotic semiconductor compounds proposed as more efficient alternatives to silicon involve the toxic elements cadmium and selenium, but the quantities are not large because of the extreme thinness of the active material (1 m^2 of a cadmium telluride cell contains a maximum of about 2 cm^3 of cadmium). Of course, multiplied by many metres squared this does add up to a potential problem. However, within the cells the material is sealed and so is isolated from the environment. Tests have shown that even in the event of fire, toxic contamination is very localized because the combustion products have low volatility. In processing, careful procedure and regular checks can minimize risks to workers, and recycling procedures have shown that very little toxic material escapes to the environment. Decommissioning of cells has also been addressed: containment and recycling of the toxic elements is quite feasible. There remains the question as to whether this will be practical on an administrative and economic basis.

6.3.2 Embodied energy and a bit more pollution

The other environmental impact comes from embodied energy. In this respect bulk processing has a much higher impact than thin film because of the higher temperatures involved. The cells are designed to save energy, so energy used in their manufacture should be minimized. The energy used to make cells derives from fossil fuels, and fossil fuels are responsible for greenhouse gas emissions and a fair amount of cadmium emission (principally from coal but also from oil). However, when the emissions resulting from the production of PV cells are compared to those for burning fossil fuels as a primary energy source, even systems based on bulk crystalline silicon are at least ten times better than fossil fuel generation per kW h of electricity produced.

The energy payback periods depend on the amount of sunlight that a module is exposed to, but the figures quoted here are based on sensible positioning in a temperate location. For crystalline silicon modules it takes about 3 to 4 years to capture more energy than was consumed in making the units. They are usually guaranteed for 10 years, and their life is expected to be around 30 years. The thin film technology-based cells, produced using lower temperature manufacturing processes, can pay back the energy consumed in production after only 2 years, though the expected life of such cells is around 20 years. So, embodied energy is recouped when cells have been generating for less than 10% of their expected life.

The other components of photovoltaic systems (support structure, inverters, wiring and installation) will also have an associated embodied energy; some of this may be offset where the PV arrays also provide a roofing or cladding material.

6.3.3 Availability of raw materials

Large scale manufacture of some types of photovoltaic cells could use large fractions of the world supply of some raw materials. The principal elements in question are indium, and to a lesser extent tellurium.

Thin film technologies are potentially affected by limited supplies of indium and similar elements because of the use of indium tin oxide for the transparent front contact layer. Whether lack of indium resources becomes a limiting problem depends on the price of these elements on the world market. A clever conservation approach is to recycle modules at the end of their life by etching off the active material, leaving the indium tin oxide intact, ready for re-use with a fresh film of semiconductor. Even so, we'd better get the research department looking at alternative transparent conductors.

Exercise 2.14

Identify where indium is used in PV.

6.4 Summary

The price of PV modules has decreased dramatically over the last few decades and thin film processes are starting to have a further effect on decreasing prices. Other components of PV systems have also to be considered and their costs reduced. The degree of financial viability of a PV system depends on subsidies and the price received for exported PV electricity.

With decreasing prices, large scale implementation becomes more plausible – most likely as grid-connected embedded generation. At a certain level of market penetration this will present problems for electricity supply because of the variability of the resource. This will require either development of long term storage technologies or the integration of PV with other renewables and cleaner fossil fuel technologies.

As with any technology there is an environmental impact. With PV this impact is nearly all in the manufacturing processes, and the bulk of this is caused by the energy used to produce the cells. However, this energy is 'paid back' within 10% of the useful life of the PV cells. The emission of pollutants and greenhouse gases associated with the manufacture and life of PV systems is less than that for the same amount of energy derived from fossil fuels.

7 Conclusion

Renewable energy technologies offer a route to reducing carbon dioxide emission and mitigating global warming, if implemented on a large scale. Any short term systems have to work within the existing infrastructure and this means a mix of renewable and non-renewable capacity.

Photovoltaics, or PV, is the most modular renewable technology that is suitable for the urban environment. Integration with other renewables enables it to contribute significantly to the reduction of greenhouse gas emissions.

The resource of solar energy is essentially inexhaustible. Sunlight comes in a continuous range of wavelengths, or photon energies, and this results in a compromise in the optimum materials employed. PV cells are made from semiconducting materials under conditions of very high purity. They are devices with no moving parts and are hence silent and almost maintenance free. There are a number of different materials employed with varying efficiencies, environmental impacts and applications.

There are parallel drives to produce either high efficiency cells by bulk crystalline processing or lower cost thin film cells with lower efficiency. The cost of the thin film technologies in particular, decreases as production increases; see ▼The next generation▲.

Applications range from stand-alone remote power systems, through power for satellites to embedded generation on domestic houses or offices. Implementation in a wider energy strategy would involve integration with energy storage mechanisms, in batteries, connection to the national grid or a chemical fuel. Economic viability remains a key issue.

> **SAQ 2.10** (Learning outcome 2.10)
>
> From the information you have gained on different material types for PV cells (Section 4) and the discussion of systems and applications (Section 5), what do you think are the main considerations for system designers in choosing cell types for particular applications?

▼The next generation▲

Thin film processing offers a big decrease in manufacturing costs when applied to large scale production. Other techniques are being researched that offer even greater reductions in cost. These include the use of semiconducting polymers and titanium dioxide activated by a light absorbent dye as the chief active materials in photocells. The deposition methods include techniques in which a paste is spread or sprayed on the substrate and then dried. These techniques are all in the next league down in terms of cost and energy, but also, unfortunately, in terms of efficiency.

8 Learning outcomes

After working through this section you should be able to:

2.1 Explain the need for renewable energy and list various options.

2.2 Summarize the advantages and disadvantages of photovoltaic technology compared with batteries, fuel cells, mains supplies, etc.

2.3 Describe the nature of sunlight as a natural resource.

2.4 Demonstrate quantitatively the potential of solar energy.

2.5 Describe the nature of specially engineered conductivity in semiconductors.

2.6 Explain how energy from light can be converted into electricity.

2.7 Show the basic principles of operation of a silicon solar cell.

2.8 Outline the manufacture of photovoltaics in bulk crystalline and thin film processes.

2.9 Describe how photovoltaic cells can be integrated into systems compatible with other power generation schemes (national grid, batteries, fuel cells).

2.10 Assess the qualitative differences between cell types and the effect of these differences on applications.

2.11 Carry out generic PV calculations.

Answers to exercises

Exercise 2.1

The temperature rise × (the number of mm of expansion per metre of depth per degree × the depth in metres) = depth increase in mm

$$0.06 \times (0.2 \times 2700) \text{ mm} = 32 \text{ mm}$$

It is clear that if the temperature of the oceans continues to rise over the next century then some lower-lying lands could literally 'go under'.

Exercise 2.2

blue: E (in eV) = $1.24/\lambda$ (in μm) = $1.24/0.50$ = 2.48 eV

green: E (in eV) = $1.24/\lambda$ (in μm) = $1.24/0.55$ = 2.25 eV

red: E (in eV) = $1.24/\lambda$ (in μm) = $1.24/0.64$ = 1.94 eV

You may want to mark these on Figure 2.7 for future reference.

Exercise 2.3

AM = $1/\cos(\theta)$ = $1/\cos(60°)$ = 2

Exercise 2.4

The SI equivalent of 2 eV is $2 \times 1.6 \times 10^{-19}$ J. The quantity we need to calculate is the number of photons per square metre per second.

The incident irradiation is 1000 W m^{-2} = 1000 J s^{-1} m^{-2}.

The average energy of each photon is $2 \times 1.6 \times 10^{-19}$ joules.

So the number of photons per square metre per second is $1000 \div (2 \times 1.6 \times 10^{-19}) = 3 \times 10^{21}$.

Exercise 2.5

To free a hole an impurity would need to have only three electrons available for the four bonds. The hole left by the missing electron could be filled by passing the shortage on to a neighbour.

Exercise 2.6

CdS, cadmium sulphide, has a threshold near the peak of the solar spectrum but that means that almost half of the photons arrive with too little energy to change the conductivity. Ge, germanium, with its low threshold can in principle absorb most of the solar spectrum.

Exercise 2.7

You may have correctly suggested one of the following:

CdS, cadmium sulphide, has a threshold near the peak of the solar spectrum.

Si and Ge would not adequately discriminate between real light and infrared emission from hot objects.

In addition, CdS is found to be better matched to the sensitivity of the film, but this is not something you are necessarily expected to know about.

Exercise 2.8

There are various ways through this problem.

For example, you could calculate the photon flux at 1360 W m^{-2} (AM0) and allow for reductions as in Section 3.3.1; then as we have just done you need an estimate of the cell e.m.f. and finally you work out the area needed for 1 kW.

An alternative is to go straight for the 14% efficiency factor and simply apply it to AM0 (which is 1360 W m^{-2}). That gives $0.14 \times 1360 \approx 200$ W m^{-2}. So about 5 m^2 of solar panels should do the job, at least while the satellite is on the sunny side of its orbit.

Exercise 2.9

The solar spectrum is spread over a range of energies. Too high a value for the threshold energy will exclude the energy available from photons with lower energies. Output power scales with the rate of photon capture.

Exercise 2.10

The output voltage from a cell scales with the threshold energy; power in turn is proportional to the output voltage. Too low a value for the threshold voltage will lead to low output power, and so relatively inefficient capture of solar power.

Exercise 2.11

(a) Silicon solar cells have a capacity to generate about 2.4 A at about 0.6 V from a device measuring 10 cm × 10 cm (see Section 3.3).

(b) Thirty such cells connected in series (so the e.m.f. of each adds together) give 2.4 A at 18 V.

(c) Three rows of ten would be easy to handle: 0.3 m × 1.0 m; any longer, narrower shapes would be difficult to handle, but five rows of six would probably be adequate: 0.5 × 0.6 m.

Exercise 2.12

(a) The total energy electrical energy I use is apparently 3347×1000 W h year^{-1} or, averaged over 365 days $(3347 \times 1000)/365$ W h day^{-1}.

(b) The AM1.5 calculations that we have done before gave a typical silicon PV output of 14 mW cm^{-2}. Taking account of the latitude of Milton Keynes (means less power per unit area) I'm going to reduce the figure and say that I can expect only 8 mW cm^{-2}. I'm also going to suggest that in this area there is an average of four hours of sunlight close to midday (a rather ambitious assumption) during which I can expect the AM1.5 conditions to apply. I can therefore hope to capture an energy per unit area of $4 \times (8 \times 10^{-3})$ W h cm^{-2} day^{-1} and after 365 days $365 \times 4 \times (8 \times 10)^{-3}$ W h cm^{-2} year^{-1}.

(c) To gather all the electrical energy I need in one year I need to deploy enough area. Let's say I need E W h year^{-1} (that's the figure calculated in (a)); the rate at which I can gather energy I'll call Y W h cm^{-2} year^{-1} (that's the figure calculated in (b)); the collection area is A cm^2. So

$E = Y A$ or $A = E/Y$ cm^2

So is that a reasonable area? Work it out; it comes out in square centimetres if you use my figures so divide by 10^4 to get a result in square metres.

$$\text{Area} = \left[\frac{(3347 \times 1000)}{(365 \times 4 \times 8 \times 10^{-3})} \right] \bigg/ 10^4 = 29 \, \text{m}^2$$

Comment: Well my roof area is only a little less than that so I'm in with a chance, provided there is a way to match the supply to the demand.

Exercise 2.13

You may have chosen two of the following:

(a) Hydro-storage is one possibility, but in the UK for instance, there are very few environmentally acceptable sites available. Long term storage is in principle possible this way.

(b) A short term, small scale solution is battery storage.
A medium term energy bank is available when electricity and water are mixed; that's something that I was always taught to avoid doing! The electrolysis of water to produce hydrogen and oxygen is a straightforward process. This is converting solar energy, through electrical energy, to 'chemical energy', if you like. The hydrogen can be stored for later use; burning it recombines it with oxygen to make water and heat energy. However, hydrogen gas itself is not easy to contain and this is a bulky way to store energy. Various techniques are being developed such as pressurization, liquefaction, adsorption on adsorbent surfaces and conversion to other fuels such as ammonia, methane or methanol – more for the research department to be getting on with.

(c) Other options might be to store energy as electric current in a ring of superconducting material; or as kinetic energy by spinning a large fly wheel (unpleasant if there is a bearing failure!).

Don't forget that the discussion here concentrates on electricity production, but the majority of energy use is as heat. You'll need to follow courses on renewable energy to see the whole picture.

Exercise 2.14

There are two areas. First, some semiconducting indium compounds are featured in Table 2.2; also, copper indium diselenide was mentioned as a potential PV material for thin film cells. Second, the transparent electrode material that is commonly used is 'indium tin oxide' (known as ITO).

Answers to self-assessment questions

SAQ 2.1

(a) Biomass, wind, solar, geothermal, hydro, tidal and wave are the principal ones. You may also have thought of ocean and thermal.

(b) There are several advantages: it is a modular system, so as many modules as required can be installed at a particular location; it is silent in operation; it is virtually maintenance free.

SAQ 2.2

Resource depletion: natural gas is forecast to run out first, oil will follow, coal reserves are good for a few centuries but will become increasingly costly to extract.

Pollution: particulates from industry and transport, and CO_2 and other greenhouse gases.

You may also have mentioned various other socio-political problems associated with energy resources being concentrated in small areas of the globe.

In this unit we are primarily interested in an engineering solution to reducing the emissions of greenhouse gases by implementation of renewable energy.

SAQ 2.3

(a) The area of the disc of the Earth that is illuminated by the Sun at any given moment is the area of a circle $= \pi \times r^2 = \pi(3.6 \times 10^6)^2$ m^2.

There are 1360 W (the solar constant) falling on each of these square metres.

Hence the total power is $\pi(3.6 \times 10^6)^2 \times 1360$ W $= 5.5 \times 10^{16}$ W or 55 000 TW (terawatts, where 1 terawatt $= 10^{12}$ watts).

(b) The surface area of the Earth is $4\pi(3.6 \times 10^6)^2$ m^2, i.e. exactly four times the area of the illuminated disc. Hence the average power over one square metre is 1360/4 W $= 340$ W.

The figure for (a) is a very large number; the Sun's power over the whole Earth is huge. It translates to 55 000 TJ every second. In fact, in one hour about the same energy falls on the Earth as human civilization produces in a whole year ($\sim 2 \times 10^{20}$ J). The answer for (b) is four times less than the peak power for two reasons. At any given time half of the surface of the Earth is not illuminated (night time). And on the illuminated side, at any given time only one point on the Earth has the Sun directly overhead; the rest has the Sun lower in the sky and so shining less energy on any given square metre.

SAQ 2.4

London latitude is 52°, some 30° beyond the tropics, therefore the effective air mass number at peak solar power $= 1/ \cos 30° = 1.15$: there is 15% more atmosphere to pass through.

SAQ 2.5

We are told we need a total power of 0.5 mW $= 5 \times 10^{-4}$ W.

We are told too that we can expect to capture 5% of 25 W for every square metre of cell. That is 1.25 W m^{-2}. The required area is

$$A = \frac{5 \times 10^{-4} \text{ W}}{1.25 \text{ W m}^{-2}} = 4 \times 10^{-4} \text{ m}^2 = 4 \text{ cm}^2$$

Thus, a strip 1 cm $\times$ 4 cm should do the job – see Figure 2.23 in Section 5.4.

SAQ 2.6

From the plot for diffuse sunlight in Northern Europe, averaging the amount of energy per month over the year gives us a value of ~1 kW h m^{-2} day^{-1}.

SAQ 2.7

(i) The semiconductor captures photons, converting their energy into freed electrons and holes.

(ii) A p–n junction then separates the electron and hole. The charge separation means that the cell can then act as a source of electricity.

SAQ 2.8

Bulk processing uses energy-intensive, process-intensive techniques to produce high quality material. This produces high efficiency material, but at high cost.

Thin film processing involves relatively low-temperature, continuous or semi-continuous processes. It produces lower quality material, and hence lower cell efficiencies, but is inherently cheaper.

SAQ 2.9

The battery requires an equivalent of 2.4 A for 10 hours to achieve a stored capacity of 24 A h. This can be provided (at the required 18 V) from five modules operating in parallel over 2 hours (the equivalent time over which the power input is 1000 W m^{-2} and so over which the output is 2.4 A).

Comment: In practice the batteries are charged from slightly higher e.m.f.s than their normal output. Nevertheless, the above argument provides a valid, if optimistic, estimate.

SAQ 2.10

The application and load to be supplied are the prime consideration, then come the area available for modules and the budget available. You could also include in your answer aspects such as ease of installation, types of system, e.g., stand-alone or grid-connected. You might also mention particular high-efficiency cells based on semiconductors other than silicon, or the flexible nature of some thin film cells. There are in fact a large number of permutations available to an engineer and a wide range of materials and systems to choose from.

Acknowledgements

Grateful acknowledgement is made to the following sources for permission to reproduce material within this block:

Part 1

Figures

Figure 1.9: Courtesy of the Trustees of the Science Museum; *Figure 1.10: Catalogue of the Great Exhibition of 1851,* David & Charles Publishers.

Part 2

Figures

Figure 2.1: Rutherford Appleton Laboratory; *Figure 2.2:* © Phototheque EDF/ Michael Brigaud; *Figure 2.10:* Reprinted from McVeigh, J. C. (1983), *Sun Power,* Elsevier Science Limited. © James McVeigh.